THE VETERINARY MEDICINES DIRECTORATE

An Executive Agency of
The Ministry of Agriculture,
Fisheries & Food

Annual Report & Accounts 1997/98

Ordered by the House of Commons to be printed 28 July 1998.

(House of Commons paper 1998 No. 814)

£15.80

1

Contents

Chief Executive's Foreword

A year of achievement and a new era

Dr. Michael Rutter

The VMD publishes its Annual Report and Accounts to

- describe the progress the Agency has made during the year;

- highlight current issues and enhance public awareness of the rigorous authorisation procedures for veterinary medicines; and

- present the VMD's audited accounts to Parliament.

1997/98 was a most significant year for the VMD. A new Government was elected in May 1997 and almost immediately published the James Report which recommended the setting up of a Food Standards Agency to restore public confidence in food safety. The James Report recommended the transfer of work on safety assessment of veterinary medicines, residues surveillance and monitoring of human suspected adverse reactions from the VMD to the new Agency. After a period of consultation, the Government proposed in its White Paper on The Food Standards Agency - A Force for Change - published in January 1998 that the VMD and its responsibilities should remain intact, but that new mechanisms and links should be introduced to ensure that the new Food Standards Agency has a significant input into the regulation of veterinary medicines. Ministers are considering the responses to the White Paper and the Goverment's conclusions will be published during the summer in the Food Standards Agency Bill. Whatever the Goverment's conclusions the VMD looks forward to working with the new Agency in taking forward the Government's policy to restore public confidence in food safety.

On 31 December 1997 the transitional arrangements for the authorisation of veterinary medicines in Europe came to an end. From 1 January 1998 a company wishing to market a product in more than one member state has to use either the centralised or the decentralised (mutual recognition) route. The new arrangements represent an exciting challenge for us. We know from our customer satisfaction consultations that we are regarded as one of the leading regulatory authorities in Europe, if not the world, and we shall be striving in 1998/99 to build on that reputation and obtain our share of work as rapporteur/co-rapporteur in the centralised procedure and as reference member state in the decentralised procedure. Co-operation with our European colleagues is an important element of the new procedures and following the success of the Veterinary Mutual Recognition Facilitation Group which we established and chaired during 1997/98, we set up during the UK presidency the Heads of European Veterinary Regulatory Agencies Group. I chaired the first meeting of this Group in February 1998 and it was agreed that at least two meetings of the Group should be held each year. Both of these Groups will contribute to the smooth running of the new European Authorisation procedures for the benefit of all.

The most tangible illustration of the new era is the VMD's new purpose-built accommodation that is being constructed adjacent to our temporary buildings on the New Haw site. This will be ready for occupation during the Summer of 1998 and will at last provide suitable accommodation for our staff and contribute to improvements in efficiency. The new accommodation will have to be paid for by higher fees and we are most grateful to all of our customers for the support they have given us during the development of this major project.

Whilst all the above developments were unfolding

our work continued to expand during 1997/98. Despite an increase of almost 27% in the volume of new licensing work, most targets were met, the backlog of variations and renewals was cleared, and first assessments of the UK's share of work on the Maximum Residue Levels (MRLs) for old substances was completed. Major new packages of legislation were introduced, a major review of non-organophosphorus sheep dips was completed and work on organophosphorus dips, antibiotic resistance and the availability of veterinary medicines continued. The results of residues surveillance in 1997 confirm that Great Britain continues to have a good record with 99.5% of more than 39,000 samples taken being free from detectable residues and the percentage of "positive" samples falling from 0.24% in 1996 to 0.13% in 1997. Work to introduce the extension of industry-funded statutory residue testing to poultry, fish, eggs, milk and farmed game has been a major task during the year, and will strengthen further our surveillance arrangements to protect the consumer.

In addition to its responsibilities for the VMD's financial and IT activities, the Business Unit has taken the lead in our work on customer satisfaction consultations, benchmarking against the European Business Excellence Model and accreditation requirements for Investors in People. The results have confirmed that the VMD has many strengths, but also highlighted some weaknesses where we need to improve. Work is in hand to address these.

Pressures on staff have continued in 1997/98 and the excellent results we have achieved are a tribute to their hard work, commitment and dedication. I cannot speak too highly of their qualities and their support. The VMD's commitment to its staff is set out in our People

Strategy in Appendix E of the Report. The year ahead will bring new challenges and opportunities - building links with the new Food Standards Agency, new European licensing work, the move into new accommodation, extended and more rigorous Ministerial targets, and the on-going public debate about organophosphorus sheep dips, antibiotic resistance, bovine somatotropin and hormones. I am confident that we shall rise to meet these challenges and make further progress towards our vision of being recognised as a world-class regulatory authority and provider of first-choice in the UK and EU for the assessment of veterinary medicinal products.

J M Rutter
June 1998

About us...

Our aims and objectives

Our Purpose

The regulation of veterinary medicines in the UK.

Our Aim

To safeguard public health, animal health and the environment and promote animal welfare.

Our Mission

To ensure the safety, quality and efficacy of all aspects of veterinary medicines in the UK.

Our Vision

To be recognised as a world-class authority for the regulation of veterinary medicinal products.

Our commitment to quality

To seek constantly to improve the quality of the service that we offer to our customers. As part of this commitment we will continue to work to the standards set out in our Customer Service Statement.[1]

To fulfil these we shall:

- achieve the financial and performance targets set by the Minister of Agriculture, Fisheries and Food and seek continual improvements in the services provided;

- administer the controls and surveillance on veterinary medicines and their residues effectively, fairly and consistently;

- deliver efficient, cost effective and high quality services to all of our customers whilst maintaining the safeguards of the licensing system;

- provide Ministers with policy advice that keeps abreast of technical progress and European Union (EU) and international requirements in the most efficient way within the resources allocated;

- participate effectively in EU and international negotiations;

- enhance confidence in licensed veterinary medicines and encourage their use by increasing public knowledge and understanding of the licensing system and post-licensing surveillance;

- apply the principles of the Citizen's Charter, in particular, to maintain or to improve the quality of services to customers, and

- maintain a highly motivated and skilled workforce.

---

[1] Copies of the VMD's Customer Service Statement are available from VMD (telephone 01932 336911)

How we are organised

Our responsibilities

The VMD is a "Next Steps" Executive Agency of the Ministry of Agriculture, Fisheries and Food (MAFF). Its formal responsibilities are set out in the VMD's Framework Document.[2]

These are:

- the authorisation and control of the manufacture and availability of veterinary medicines;

- post authorisation surveillance of suspected adverse reactions and residues of veterinary products in meat and animal products; and

- the provision and implementation of policy advice on these matters to the Agriculture and Health Ministers who jointly form the licensing authority.

The VMD fulfils these responsibilities by using its expertise to validate, assess and interpret written information on veterinary medicines. Independent expert advice is provided by the Veterinary Products Committee (VPC)[3] and the Medicines Commission (MC).[4] Where physical tests or other procedures have to be carried out these are normally sub-contracted.

Dr. Michael Rutter   Steve Dean   John FitzGerald   Ray Anderson

Our structure

The Minister of Agriculture, Fisheries and Food is accountable to Parliament for the activities of the VMD. The Chief Executive is directly responsible to the Minister for the day to day operation of the VMD as set out in the VMD's Framework Document. The VMD's Ownership Board[5] monitors the agency's performance. The Chief Executive is supported by a Director of Licensing, a Director of Policy and the VMD Secretary and Head of the Business Unit.

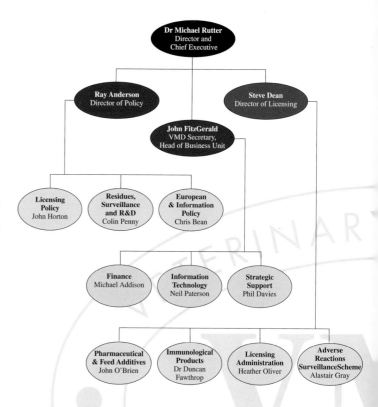

Our people

On 31 March 1998 the VMD employed 113 full and part-time permanent staff including veterinarians, pharmacists, toxicologists, biologists, IT specialists, administrative and support staff.

2   Copies of this document are available from VMD (telephone 01932 336911).
3   The VPC's membership and terms of reference are detailed at Appendix B.
4   Copies of the Annual Report of the Medicine Commission can be obtained from The Stationary Office Ltd at the addresses shown on the rear cover of this Report.
5   The membership and terms of Reference for this Board are detailed at Appendix A.

Our Work

The VMD's work divides into three main areas, or "businesses":

- **Licensing** – the assessment of applications, issue of marketing authorisations and surveillance of suspected adverse reactions to veterinary medicines, licensing and inspecting veterinary medicine manufacturers and inspecting wholesale dealers;

- **Residues** – surveillance for residues of veterinary medicines in meat and animal products, reporting of results and co-ordination of follow-up action;

- **Policy** – servicing, developing and implementing new policy/legislation on all aspects of veterinary medicines in the UK; providing support to Ministers through briefings and advice on correspondence and Parliamentary Questions; day to day management of veterinary medicines R&D programme on behalf of the Ministry of Agriculture, Fisheries and Food.

In addition a **Business Unit** provides corporate services e.g. IT, Finance, Human Resources and information to customers about VMD's activities and achievements.

Our finances

The cost of running the VMD's operation during 1997/98 was £8.6 million. The VMD seeks to recover, through charges to its customers, the full costs of the services it provides.

Average staff numbers 1997/98

Licensing

Policy and Residues

Business Unit

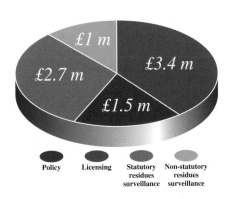

Our work in 1997/98

Director of Licensing's Review

Steve Dean

We have made excellent progress this year in reducing the levels of assessment work outstanding and preparing for an expanded rôle within the European regulatory framework.

- **Assessments**: during the year we successfully focused considerable effort on completing assessments of outstanding variations and renewals. We are now able to complete primary assessment of variations and renewals within 75 and 90 days respectively, from the time a valid application is accepted. In the coming year we are confident that we will extend this service so that all variations and renewals will complete their full assessment by 150 or 180 days respectively (excluding time that responses to questions are awaited from the company).

  On the 1 January 1998, the mutual recognition procedure became mandatory and the predicted peak of applications was received in December 1997. This prevented significant progress on outstanding national applications, but it is intended these will be the major focus in 1998/99.

- **Staffing issues**: this year we have had a full complement of staff in all teams, which together with the employment of temporary and consultancy staff, has been a major factor in our success in reducing outstanding assessment work. We have added to our expertise in the pharmaceutical group principally in the Quality team and in ecotoxicology. We have also strengthened our Pharmacovigilance team in preparation for its expanding European rôle. The VMD is well placed

to fulfil its responsibilities and will continue improving the service it offers to the pharmaceutical industry.

- **European applications:** we gained further experience in the centralised procedure and the mutual recognition process during the year. The UK acted as a reference member state under the mutual recognition procedure on 17 occasions. In April 1997 the Veterinary Mutual Recognition Facilitation Group was formed and the UK was asked to chair the meetings by the Netherlands and Luxembourg during their presidencies. This chairmanship has continued during the UK presidency and the Austrian authorities have asked the UK to continue during their presidency, up until December 1998.

- the UK has acted as rapporteur in the setting of Maximum Residue Limits (MRLs) for a significant proportion of old active ingredients. The assessment of data submitted in support of these applications was completed in March 1998.

- the immunological review has progressed well during the year. We have dedicated a small team of three assessors to this task, and, as a result, the primary assessment of review dossiers was completed by the end of March 1998. The focus for the coming year will be the assessment of responses to questions.

development work commenced this year on a new database for the **Suspected Adverse Reactions Surveillance Scheme (SARSS).** The project is well advanced and the database is now being used in parallel with the old existing database and is expected to be fully operational by July 1998. The new database is expected to improve the monitoring of suspected adverse reactions and will help the VMD fulfil its Pharmacovigilance rôle within the European Union.

- Members of the licensing team have continued to contribute scientific advice to the policy group and, in particular, have carried out work in relation to the organophosphorus (OP) sheep dips, antibiotic resistance, availability of medicines and the use of the zootechnical feed additives.

- All but one of the targets set for licensing were met during the year. We did not achieve the first assessment of 100% of new applications for variations or renewals within 75 and 90 days respectively. This was chiefly because of unexpectedly high numbers of submissions during the year, but the spirit of the target was achieved, in that no variations or renewals were outstanding beyond these times by the end of 1997/98.

  The outstanding success of the licensing effort during the year is principally due to the dedication and hard work of the scientists with excellent support from their colleagues in administration. I would like to acknowledge this commendable performance and pay tribute to the hard work and dedication of the entire licensing team.

Applications determined

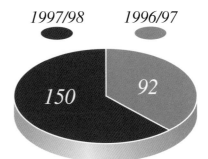

1997/98   *1996/97*

National Marketing Authorisations

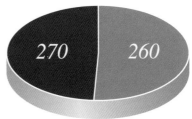

Renewals

Variations

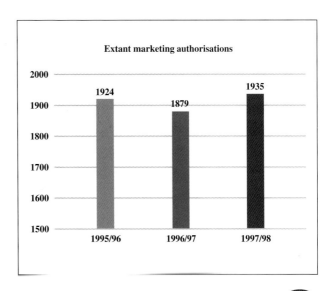

Director of Policy's Review

Ray Anderson

This has been a year of significant progress for the policy and residues business in taking forward all areas of work.

● The implementation of legislation to extend the ban on the use of hormones and beta agonists and to reinforce the requirements for residues surveillance programmes.

● Substantial work on the implementation of EC Directives covering zootechnical feed additives and medicated feedingstuffs and the implications for those changes on the legal classification of products for the purpose of distribution.

● Making changes to simplify existing legislation and adapting it to take account of European case law, notably on personal imports of veterinary medicines.

● The completion of a major review by the Veterinary Products Committee on the safety of non-organophosphorus sheep dips and the acceptance of all of the VPC's recommendations by the Government. Work was put in hand to implement these recommendations which involve some changes to legislation to improve the controls over the sale and disposal of these products.

● Commissioning further research in support of policy advice to Ministers on the safety of organophosphorus sheep dips. The work is concentrating on possible mechanisms of toxicity of organophosphates.

● Making major adjustments to the residues surveillance programmes to reflect the requirements of the new legislation which includes the levying of charges on the poultry, farmed fish, milk, eggs and wild and farmed game industries.

In addition, there was a high level of Parliamentary and public interest in the possibility of transfer of resistance to antibiotics from animal pathogens to man and the VMD provided evidence and other inputs to investigations by Select Committees, the Advisory Committee on the Microbiological Safety of Food and, internationally, to the European Commission's Committee on Veterinary Medicinal Products and the World Health Organisation. Other issues included the availability of medicines for horses and continued interest in the safety of organophosphorus sheep dips. The VMD was represented on an Interdepartmental Committee on organophosphates which was set up by Ministers in December 1997.

Outputs continued to reflect the continuing high level of public interest in VMD's areas of responsibility:

	1995/96	1996/97	1997/98
Parliamentary Questions	138	105	63
Ministers Correspondence	813	193	394
Briefs and submissions	1390	1212	1594
Total	**2341**	**1510**	**2051**
Statutory Instruments	5	10	10

VMD Secretary and Head of Business Unit's Review

John FitzGerald

The Business Unit has helped to bring about significant change this year for the VMD. The most noticeable has been our new office block rising out of the rubble of the old farm manager's house, which had to be demolished before construction work could begin. We should be able to move into our new building in the summer of 1998. After seven years of working in up to six "temporary" buildings the move into more suitable accommodation will help the VMD to provide a more efficient service to all of our customers.

The IT team and Finance group worked together to introduce our new IT operating system based on SQL servers and Microsoft Windows NT. This has enabled a new relational database to be developed for recording suspected adverse reactions and the upgrading of the SUNACCOUNTS system which was needed to cope with the increased accounting work which will result from the extended statutory residues surveillance scheme. The new operating structure is also an integral element of our plans for ensuring that the VMD's IT systems are millennium compliant.

As part of the VMD's plans to improve staff development and meet Investors in People standards, all staff completed personal development plans to identify their training needs for the first time this year. We also consulted staff on their views of the VMD and look forward to receiving the analysis of their comments early in 1998/99. The need for this survey was identified from benchmarking the VMD against the European Business Excellence Model as part of a Cabinet Office project. This gave us valuable information which helped prioritise our plans and should enable us to develop ideas from those agencies or companies who scored well in the areas where we did not.

Change can be unsettling but the staff of the Business Unit continue to work with great enthusiasm and success both when coping with change themselves and helping others to introduce it. I am grateful for all of their efforts and their positive attitude which helps to make VMD an enjoyable place to work.

Pursuing our aims and objectives

Achieving agreed targets and seeking continual improvements

Each year the Minister of Agriculture, Fisheries and Food sets a number of challenging performance targets for the VMD. We aim to achieve these targets and to continually improve the quality of the services we offer to our customers.

Achieving our 1997/98 targets

This section shows our achievements against the 1997/98 performance targets announced to Parliament on 20 March 1997.[6]

Financial

Target: To recover from industry and Government the full economic cost of each of its main business activities of:

- licensing and surveillance
- policy work
- residue monitoring.

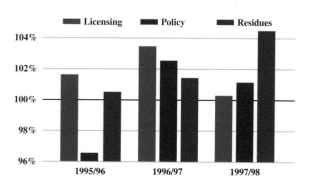

Target: To operate within the net cash allocation as agreed by the MAFF Management Board.

Quality of Service

Target: To deliver high quality policy advice to Ministers

Target: To deliver high quality scientific work

Target: To determine 80% of new marketing authorisations within 120 clock days; 95% within 200 clock days.

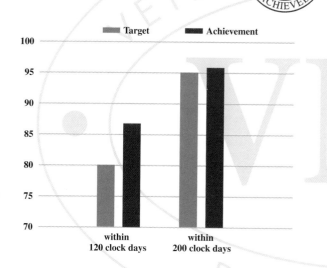

[6] More details on how we monitor and assure our performance against our performance targets are included on page 23.

Target: To ensure that the first assessment of variations outstanding for more than 75 clock days on 1 April 1997 is completed by 31 October 1997.

TARGET ACHIEVED

As this record shows, 1997/98 was a very successful year for the VMD during which we achieved six and two thirds of the seven performance targets set for us by Ministers.[7] This was a considerable achievement given the nearly 27% overall increase in new licensing work in 1997/98.

and that a first assessment of renewals outstanding for more than 90 days on 1 April 1997 is completed by 31 December 1997;

TARGET ACHIEVED

and to ensure that first assessments for variations and renewals arriving after 1 April 1997 are completed within 75 and 90 clock days respectively.

Not achieved

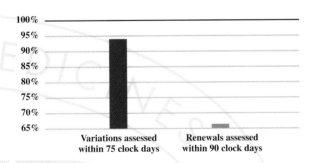

Target: To meet target timescales for centralised, decentralised and MRL applications under EU procedures.

TARGET ACHIEVED

7   The detailed figures on the VMD's performance against targets during 1997/98 are set out at Appendix C.

13

Seeking continual improvement

To serve our customers better we must continually improve our understanding of their needs. To this end we employed independent management consultants this

Customer consultations

year to carry out **customer consultations** of our external customers on our work on licensing and residue surveillance. The very high response rate (between 40-51%) demonstrated a high level of interest in our services. The very positive results from these surveys and from an earlier survey of customers of our Policy Business in MAFF and outside organisations, were reported to the VMD's Ownership Board in February 1998.

Quality workshops

We also organised two **quality workshops** to look at how to improve our communications and assure the quality of our service. These were amongst the issues identified in November 1996 as most likely to affect us over the following five years. On both occasions we were very happy to welcome a guest speaker from our customers.

Benchmarking

In addition this year the VMD took part in a Cabinet Office **benchmarking** exercise which compared Government Agencies against the European Business Excellence Model (BEM). This aims to assist Agencies in identifying and prioritising their development opportunities. During July 1997 a small team from across the VMD answered more than 100 questions. Their answers were used to identify the VMD's strengths and weaknesses, and to draw up a prioritised action plan.

The results from all of these exercises have been reported to staff and fully integrated into the agency's **strategic planning** processes so that we can meet our aim to continually improve our services to customers. We intend to repeat them on a regular basis.

Administering controls
effectively, fairly and consistently

A key feature of the controls on veterinary medicines is the marketing authorisation which is required before a product can be placed on the market in the EU. Marketing authorisations are granted only after a product has undergone a rigorous assessment to establish its safety, quality and efficacy. We aim to administer these controls and conduct our work on post authorisation surveillance[8] in an effective, fair and consistent manner.

To achieve this we subject our work to ongoing independent expert review and internal audit. We also seek to ensure consistent adherence to the marketing authorisations we issue through a worldwide inspection programme of premises manufacturing veterinary medicines for use in the UK and by enforcing controls on their distribution. We monitor the effects of the use of veterinary medicines to make sure that our controls remain effective. We also regularly review and update legislation to ensure that it remains relevant and in line with EU requirements.

Seeking independent scrutiny and advice

The VMD's administration of controls on veterinary medicines and work on post authorisation surveillance is subject to independent scrutiny and advice by committees and groups established for this purpose.[9] This ensures that we continue to undertake all of our responsibilities effectively, fairly and consistently.

The Veterinary Products Committee (VPC)

The **Veterinary Products Committee (VPC)** is a statutory body constituted under Section 4 of the Medicines Act 1968 to advise Ministers on the safety, quality and efficacy of veterinary medicines and promote collection of information relating to suspect adverse reactions. Members are appointed for their expertise in disciplines relevant to human, animal health and the environment. The VPC held ten meetings in 1997 at which assessment reports and advice from VMD officials were considered. Committee members also evaluated the quality of the VMD's scientific advice to enable the Chairman to report to the Minister on achievement against the "quality of scientific advice" target. Summaries of the proceedings of each meeting were issued this year as News Releases within one week from the meeting. These gave brief details of the applications considered and of other items not subject to commercial confidentiality. A full report of the VPC's work is published in the Medicines Act 1968 Advisory Bodies Annual Report 1997.[10]

---

8 More detail on the structure of these controls is available in the booklet "The Work of the Veterinary Medicines Directorate", which is available from VMD (telephone 01932 336911).
9 The terms of reference and current membership for each of these independent committees are set out at Appendix B.
10 Copies of this report are available from The Stationary Office Ltd at the addresses shown on the rear cover of this Report.

The Advisory Group on Veterinary Residues (AGVR)

The **Advisory Group on Veterinary Residues** (AGVR) was established in 1995 to advise the VMD on its veterinary residue surveillance programmes. It is made up from independent members with expertise in consumer, analytical and veterinary matters as well as members from representative industry organisations. The AGVR met three times in 1997 to scrutinise and give advice on the results of the surveillance programmes. They also agreed the second Annual Report on Surveillance for Veterinary Residues, which was published in July 1997. Their third Annual Report will be published at the same time as this Report.[11]

The Appraisal Panel on Human Suspected Adverse Reactions

The Appraisal Panel on Human Suspected Adverse Reactions continued to evaluate all suspected adverse reactions to veterinary medicinal products in humans. New independent members were added to the panel this year. The panel met five times during the year to look at trends and signals of emergent problems, consider their possible causes, monitor the consequences of recommendations for changes in working practices or use and report its findings to the VPC.[12] A report of the panel's findings from meetings held in 1996 was published in January 1998.

Internal audit

Internal audits were carried out during the year by MAFF auditors on the VMD's work on IT millennium compliance, VAT and financial planning and budgetary control. No significant issues were identified. Work was also started during the year on internal audits on the VMD's licensing work and our move to the new building.

Controlling the manufacture of veterinary medicines

Controls over the manufacture of veterinary medicines ensure that authorised products meet the specifications set out in the marketing authorisation.

GMP (Good Manufacturing Practice) scheme

Veterinary medicines must be manufactured in accordance with **GMP (Good Manufacturing Practice).** This year the VMD and the Medicines Control Agency on our behalf undertook 47 inspections worldwide of premises authorised to manufacture veterinary medicines for the UK market. These checked that the premises were suitable for the production of safe, effective veterinary medicines of a consistently high standard, and that the medicines were being manufactured in accordance with their marketing authorisations. Ten of these inspections were carried out by VMD staff.

[11] Copies of the Annual Report on Surveillance for Veterinary Residues in 1997 are available from VMD (telephone 01932 336911)
[12] The membership and terms of reference of this panel are detailed at Appendix B.

QA/QC (Quality Assurance/Quality Control) scheme

VMD staff also carried out 36 inspections during the year under our **QA/QC (Quality Assurance/Quality Control) scheme.** This ensures that the testing of each batch of an immunological product is appropriate, consistent, of suitable sensitivity and that there is confidence in the data of the batch test protocols. These inspections examined each company's quality control facilities and batch testing procedures to ensure that if a batch were defective it would be picked up before it was released for sale. Companies participating in this scheme who wish to sell batches of UK authorised products in other EU member states need to obtain EU Batch Release Certificates from the VMD. VMD issued 118 certificates this year, all within 48 hours of receiving the batch protocol.

Inspections under the QA/QC Scheme

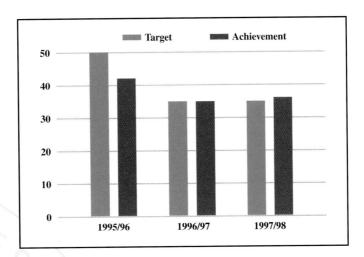

Controlling the distribution of veterinary medicines

Controls on the distribution of veterinary medicines seek to ensure that they are sold, or supplied, only by people with specialist knowledge of how best to use them, or advise on their use.

Wholesalers of veterinary medicines are licensed by the VMD. Retail sale or supply of veterinary medicines may be made by veterinarians, by pharmacists, or for certain listed products (the Merchants' List), by agricultural merchants or saddlers registered with the Royal Pharmaceutical Society of Great Britain (RPSGB). Some veterinary medicines (General Sale List or GSL) may be sold without restriction, for

Monitoring and enforcement

example in supermarkets or pet shops. Proper **monitoring and enforcement** ensure that the legislative controls on distribution are applied fairly and consistently. Wholesalers are inspected on VMD's behalf by the Medicines Control Agency. The Animal Medicines Inspectorate of the RPSGB checks the retail supply of Merchants List and GSL products on VMD's behalf. Alleged breaches of the law reported to the VMD may be investigated by MAFF's Investigation Branch and where there is sufficient evidence, will be taken to court. At the end of March 1998 there were six active investigations under way and during the year one case was successfully prosecuted and the defendant fined £2,500 with £3,000 costs.

Monitoring the effects of the use of veterinary medicines

The VMD undertakes surveillance to monitor for any unwanted effects resulting from the use of veterinary medicines, both from suspected adverse reactions and residues of veterinary drugs in food.

Suspected Adverse Reaction Surveillance Scheme (SARSS)

The **Suspected Adverse Reaction Surveillance Scheme (SARSS)** records reports of suspect adverse reactions (SARs) to veterinary medicines in animals and humans received from veterinary surgeons, the public or marketing authorisations holders. All serious reactions reported to the VMD were reviewed monthly to try to identify developing trends and whether any action was required, and reported quarterly to the VPC.

SARs involving humans

229 reports of **SARs involving humans** were received in 1997/98. 166 of these related to ectoparasiticide products, 30 involved organophosphorus sheep dips and 11 involved other veterinary medicines containing organophosphates.

SARs involving animals

The number of reports of **SARs involving animals** continued to increase this year, in particular those from veterinary surgeons and companies. This may reflect an increasing public awareness of the possibility of reactions to ectoparasiticides, particularly those in companion animals.

	1995/96	1996/97	1997/98
Overall total	1,385	1,441	1,896
Reports from veterinary surgeons, farmers, general public and individual company reports	965	1,094	1,565

Reports relating to cats and dogs continued to form the bulk of reports, although the number relating to rabbits continued to increase as the number of treatments used in this species increased.

	1995/96	1996/97	1997/98
Dog	347	365	591
Cat	271	381	570
Horse	120	71	93
Cow	90	81	87
Sheep	47	73	62
Pig	18	14	10
Rabbit	41	67	103
Poultry	15	1	2
Fish	5	27	30
Other	13	14	17

The following page shows the distribution of suspected adverse reactions by therapeutic group in 1996/97 and 1997/98.

The VMD made a major contribution this year to the development of EU guidelines for pharmaceutical companies on reporting and recording suspected adverse reactions.

A guidance document was issued on 1 January 1998 describing the intended scope of European pharmacovigilance, which will include as new areas:

● epidemiosurveillance of resistance;

● potential environmental problems; and

● reported violations of approved residue limits.

Distribution of suspected
adverse reactions by
therapeutic group

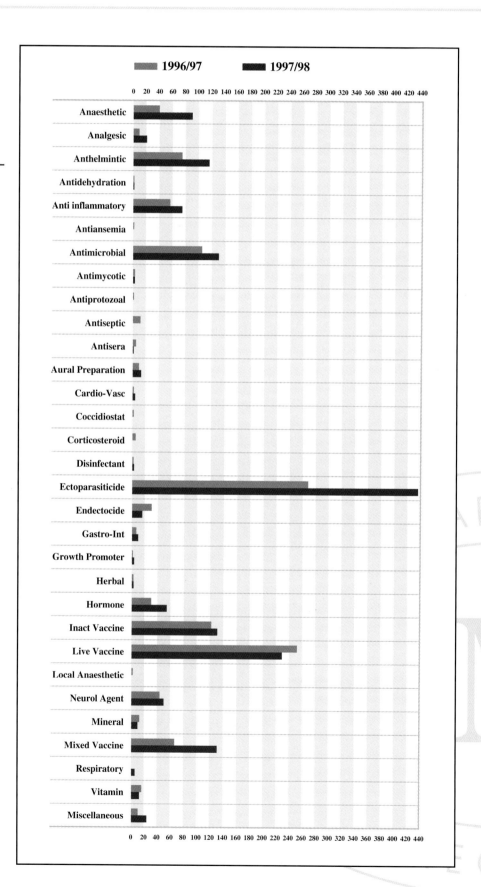

A new relational computer database was developed for SARSS during the year which will help us to undertake more effective analysis of the information received through the scheme. Consequential work was also carried out to revise the yellow report form and the SARSS leaflet, including improvements to the publicity aimed to encourage the reporting of human SARs through doctors.

The VMD's SARSS team also made valuable new contacts this year with various other scientific bodies and agencies including the Ministry of Agriculture for New Zealand and the US Food and Drug Administration.

Surveillance for residues of veterinary medicines in food

Statutory residues surveillance programme

Surveillance for residues of veterinary medicines in food is undertaken under the statutory and non statutory veterinary residues surveillance programmes.[13] The VMD co-ordinates and manages these two complementary programmes which monitor, respectively, residues in red meat and in other animal products. Both programmes are overseen by the AGVR. The **statutory residues surveillance programme** tested 39,652 samples in 1997 (excluding cadmium in horses) of which some 39,454 (99.5%) were free from detectable residues. All of the costs of this sampling were met by statutory charges levied on slaughterhouse operators. Samples were taken from randomly selected farms and slaughterhouses in GB. Follow up action was taken on all positive samples. Two cases resulted in successful prosecutions.

Non-statutory residues surveillance programme

The **non-statutory surveillance programme** covers animal products and veterinary medicines not included within the statutory surveillance programme. It is funded entirely by the Ministry of Agriculture, Fisheries and Food and aims to give information on the nature and incidence of residues in products on sale or to be sold to the consumer. No residues above the action level were detected in 99.5% of analyses undertaken under this scheme in 1997.

Toxicologists in the VMD and the Department of Health have advised that none of the residues found under either programme this year would have posed any risk to human health.

---

[13] Greater detail of these programmes, including the results for 1997, can be found in the Annual Report on Surveillance for Veterinary Medicines in 1997, copies available from VMD (telephone 01932 336911)

Reviewing and updating legislation

We continued this year to review the legislation controlling the manufacture and distribution of veterinary medicines. Major reviews were undertaken of the legislation affecting the manufacture and distribution of medicated animal feedingstuffs and zootechnical feed additives, and the Merchants' List. These resulted in new legislation coming into effect in May 1998. Some minor changes to legislation were also necessitated by the introduction of a simplified registration scheme for homoeopathic veterinary medicinal products last year. The first of these set a default category of GSL for registered homoeopathic products whilst the second categorised certain homoeopathic products as PML. New regulations entered into force on 1 February 1998 which prohibited personal imports of products which are not authorised in the UK. These regulations also allowed the use of comparator products authorised elsewhere in the EU under EC legislation.

Delivering efficient, cost effective and high quality customer services

We use a number of mechanisms to assure the quality, efficiency and cost effectiveness of our service delivery to our customers These include target setting and strategic and financial planning. We also aim to provide our staff with the right tools and environment for them to deliver an efficient, quality service to our customers.

Target setting and strategic planning

Ministers annually set **performance targets** for the VMD. Those set for 1997/98, and our achievement against them, are set out on pages 12 and 13. We also set individual workplans for each business through an annual **Strategic Planning** process. Each Spring we publish a Corporate Plan which sets out briefly our strategy for assuring our service delivery over the mid-term future. The **Three Year Corporate Plan** for the period 1997/98-1999/2000 was published in April 1997.[14] We also issue a **One Year Business Plan** to all our staff, which details the performance and financial targets for the coming year, our objectives and workplans and the resources estimated necessary to meet them. Copies of the VMD's One Year Business Plan for 1997/98 were circulated to all VMD staff in April 1997.[15]

Delivering services to our customers

Assessing applications for marketing authorisations

This year we received nearly 36% more **applications for new marketing authorisations** than last year. The increase in the number received in December was far in excess of that anticipated. This was probably due to companies anticipating the changes in EU rules on marketing authorisations which came into effect from 1 January 1998. These changes meant that from that date all applications to market veterinary medicinal products in more than one EU member state have had to go through the decentralised procedure. However by employing extra staff to assist with this influx and with the dedication and hard work of all those involved, we were still able to meet many of our Licensing Business targets.

Applications Received since 31 March 1997

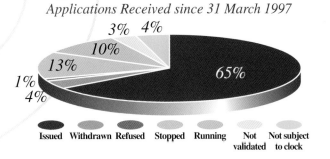

Issued Withdrawn Refused Stopped Running Not validated Not subject to clock

[14] Copies of this Plan are available from VMD (telephone 01932 36911)
[15] Because of the commercial confidentiality of some of the information contained in this Plan it is only available to VMD staff.

Immunological products

At the start of the year there were 139 applications for **immunological products** being assessed or awaiting responses to requests for further information. During the year we received a further 33 applications for marketing authorisations for immunological products and 209 and 59 applications respectively for variations and renewals to existing marketing authorisations for immunological products. By the end of the year over 78% of these had been determined and only 97 applications were still being assessed or awaiting further information from the applicant.

We also made considerable efforts this year to assist applicants using the centralised and decentralised application procedures. We acted as rapporteur for an application for the first veterinary product to go through the centralised procedure, under Part B of the Annex to Council Regulation 2309/93/EEC[16] which was successfully completed within the required timescale. We also dealt with a further four applications for immunological products under the centralised procedure, where the UK was not acting as rapporteur or co-rapporteur. As predicted there was an increase in activity on decentralised applications for immunological products , where the UK acted as reference member state for two applications during the year. In addition there were four applications for decentralised variations where the UK acted as reference member state and three for variations where the UK acted as concerned member state.

This year also saw the completion of initial assessment of immunological products under the review required by Directive 81/851/EEC. This will help companies currently marketing immunological products in the UK to apply for decentralised applications.

Pharmaceutical and feed additives

We received 175 applications for marketing authorisations for **pharmaceuticals and feed additives** during the year. All national applications received in December 1997 were validated during the early part of January 1998.

The majority of variation applications related to the chemistry and pharmacy part of the marketing authorisation dossier and were dealt with by the pharmacy assessors only. We were able to achieve our target for outstanding variation applications by taking on temporary staff in the pharmacy group and by the early appointment of a new permanent member of staff before his predecessor retired. The contribution of the

[16] An immunological products which qualifies under Part B is one which has either been developed, manufactured or is to be used in an innovative manner or one which contains an active ingredient which has not previously been authorised for use in food producing animals.

temporary staff was also a significant factor in helping us achieve the target for outstanding renewal applications.

The demands of the work required for centralised and decentralised applications, however, meant that we were unable to meet our targets for variations and renewals received during 1997-1998.

We dealt with one application under the centralised procedure, and acted as reference member state for 17 applications. We also dealt with four applications for Maximum Residue Limits (MRLs) as rapporteur or co-rapporteur and completed assessment of 26 applications for MRLs for existing substances. All of these applications were dealt with within the prescribed timescales.

Marketing authorisation progress tracking systems

Refinements were also made this year to the **marketing authorisation progress tracking systems** which regularly record and report to management on the progress of all marketing authorisation applications. This system helps to ensure that proper priority is given to each application.

Reporting results from residues surveillance

All **results from residues surveillance**, under both programmes, were notified to the shop or slaughterhouse from which the samples were taken within 10 working days of the end of the period being reported on this year.

Providing staff with the right tools and environment

Equally important in assuring a quality service to customers was the work carried out this year to provide staff with the right tools and environment for them to deliver their best work. These include sound IT and financial systems which provide appropriate management information, and suitable accommodation.

Information Technology

Our **Information Technology** strategy is aimed to support our business objectives and to provide staff with an IT environment which supports their individual and team efforts to provide a quality service to our customers.

The current Information Systems architecture can be represented as:

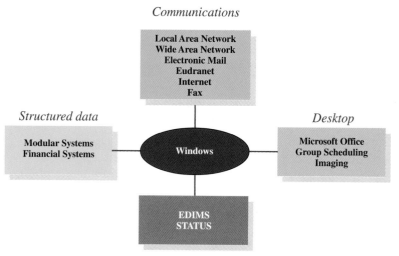

Communications

Local Area Network
Wide Area Network
Electronic Mail
Eudranet
Internet
Fax

Structured data

Modular Systems
Financial Systems

Windows

Desktop

Microsoft Office
Group Scheduling
Imaging

EDIMS
STATUS

Structured information

Developments during the year have been aimed at providing:

- millennium compliance;

- systems which can meet the many new requirements arising out of the changes to the VMD business sectors;

- compatibility with European systems, i.e. EudraWatch and EudraTrack.

We have adopted the Dynamic Systems Development Method for delivering bespoke Information Systems. The principal tools are Joint Application Design and Prototyping with the aim of rapid and incremental deployment of new systems.

Structured Information

In the **Structured Information** area this year we have selected the products to replace the existing Electronic Document and Image Management system.

Structured Data

In the **Structured Data** area the in-house Rapid Application Development (RAD) tools are now Object Oriented around the Microsoft Common Object Model and ActiveX component based architecture. The Pharmacovigilance system has been used to create a new RAD application template. Financial systems have been upgraded to run on Windows NT/SQL server which supports Millennium and Euro compliant versions of the Sunaccounts software. The Statutory Residues Surveillance IT system has been extensively developed to support major extensions to the scheme and increased reporting facilities.

Communications

Communications have been improved this year through the connection to the MAFF intranet provided on the desktop. A leased line has also been installed to better support the heavier use of the EudraNet, the European network.

Desktop

Work also commenced this year on upgrading the **Desktop** operating system from Microsoft Windows 3.1 to Microsoft Windows NT 4 to be millennium compliant and to provide a platform for the business tools required by our staff.

Finance and accounting

The VMD's **finance and accounting** systems are designed to:

● maintain proper accounting records, invoice our customers and pay our properly incurred liabilities; and

● keep VMD senior management and the Minister fully informed of our performance against targets, financial condition and provide the financial input to our planning processes.

Accounting systems

During 1997/98 the **accounting systems**, based upon Systems Union's "Sunaccounts" accounting software package, were upgraded to operate with a full graphic user interface on Microsoft's NT4 operating system utilising Microsoft Structured Query Language (SQL) architecture. This brings significant benefits, not only in operator usability but also in the accessibility of the accounting information. With this arrangement it will be possible for management and other users of information to access relevant databases directly without having to go through the accounting systems. One of the more immediate benefits achieved has been the removal of several layers of duplication in the cash office systems prior to experiencing the increase in volume resulting from the extension of the statutory residues scheme.

Credit control

With the extension of the statutory residues scheme to poultry, fish, eggs, milk and farmed game, the opportunity has been taken to install specialised **credit control** add-ons to the accounting systems. This enables credit control staff to control, through the accounting system, all credit control processes with a system of allocation markers, progress "flags" and a note-taking capability on individual transactions as well as on accounts. Credit control reporting capabilities have also been signicantly improved.

In the near future it is intended to capitalise on the SQL architecture by distributing report templates to management and other recipients of management information to enable instantaneous reporting of specific areas with a full "drill-down" capability.

Work recording

The **work recording** system will also be upgraded to incorporate direct input to the system by the users themselves, subject to full accounting control, through well established professionally written time sheet software.

Cash office

With the advent of the new building, a purpose built **cash office** will be made available to the accounting team which should enable the VMD to operate all its cash payments systems entirely independently of the main Ministry accounting systems. This will bring the benefits of a more immediate and responsive payments system to the VMD's suppliers.

Accommodation

The scattered nature of our **accommodation** has made it difficult to do even the simplest tasks efficiently, such as moving dossiers and other papers between colleagues, especially in inclement weather! The limited overall space meant that many papers had to be stored off site. Retrieving these took time and reduced efficiency. Building work started in September 1997 on a new office block to accommodate the whole of VMD.

Our new office block had to be built within a budget of £3.5 million but will be a vast improvement on our previous accommodation. All staff will be located in the new three storey office block on our current site. The building will have modern storage facilities, more working and meeting space and a dedicated telephone system with direct dialling in and voice mail. This should make it easier for customers to contact the VMD, helping to address one of the issues identified in the customer consultations (see page 14).

Providing Ministers with sound policy advice

We aim to provide Ministers with appropriate advice on all aspects of veterinary medicines to enable them to take properly informed policy decisions. We ensure that such advice is based on the most up to date science and that it is delivered on time. We also seek the views of independent experts where this will improve the quality of our advice.

Advancing the scientific foundation

In a fast moving area like veterinary medicines it is important to base policy on a sound understanding of the science which influences their safety, quality and efficacy. During 1997/98 the VMD, in co-operation with the Ministry of Agriculture, Fisheries and Food's Chief Scientist's Group, co-ordinated and managed the Ministry's R&D programme on veterinary medicines.[17] This continues to comprise mainly short term research in three areas:

- research in support of the assurance of the quality of immunological veterinary medicines-1997/98 estimated cost £330,000

- research into aspects of residues of veterinary medicines in meat and animal products-1997/98 estimated cost £1,414,000; and

- an epidemiological study on the possible chronic effects on humans resulting from contact with organophosphorus sheep dips. This project is jointly funded with the Health and Safety Executive and the Department of Health.

Assuring timeliness

To be of value policy advice must also be timely. There were continued improvements this year in the turnaround of responses to requests for draft Ministerial replies to Parliamentary Questions, correspondence from Members of Parliament and the public and briefing and other policy advice. As the table on the next page shows, the target of 95% was exceeded with all replies but one being returned on time.

---

[17] Greater detail on these programmes, incluyding the results for 1997, is available in the Annual Report on Surveillance for Veterinary Medicines in 1997, available from VMD (telephone 01932 336911)

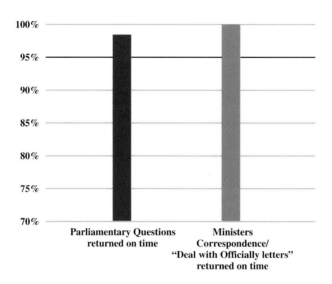

In addition, the delivery of results in relation to legislative and other programmes was improved through the introduction of project management procedures to plan and allocate resources. Some of the new legislation was introduced shortly after the target dates due to factors outside VMD's control, such as the General Election.

Seeking independent advice

The VMD seeks independent scientific advice on policy issues from the Veterinary Products Committee, the Advisory Group on Veterinary Residues, and other advisory committees. This year the VPC carried out reviews and provided advice on the use of non-organophosphorus sheep dips and on antimicrobial resistance.

Participating effectively in EU and international negotiations and discussions

We continued this year to ensure an effective UK contribution to EU and international negotiations and discussions through our close involvement in a wide range of European and other international bodies.

Working in Europe

Decisions taken by various pan-European institutions are an increasingly important element in the control of veterinary medicines. The VMD participates in the discussions leading to these decisions and aims to ensure that they facilitate the authorisation of safe and effective medicines in the UK and EU markets.

Heads of European Veterinary Regulatory Agencies

The introduction of new European licensing procedures from 1 January 1998 focused attention on the need for a forum where **Heads of European Veterinary Regulatory Agencies** could discuss areas of common interest in relation to their responsibilities for procedures under Community legislation for the authorisation of veterinary medicines. With the support of colleagues in other member states, the UK set up the Heads of European Veterinary Regulatory Agencies Group during 1997/98 and Dr Rutter chaired its first meeting on 18 February 1998 in London. Matters discussed included ways to improve the decentralised (mutual recognition) procedure, resources required by member states in relation to the centralised procedure and the IT network for European licensing. The Group agreed that in future it should meet twice a year in London with the Chairmanship rotating with the EU Presidency and that additional meetings would be arranged as necessary.

European Medicines Evaluation Agency

The **European Medicines Evaluation Agency (EMEA)'s Committee for Veterinary Medicinal Products (CVMP)** and its working groups are responsible for preparing scientific opinions on the evaluation of veterinary products and advising the EMEA on any scientific issues which arise on the use and marketing of certain veterinary medicinal products.[18] Dr Michael Rutter and Jill Ashley-Smith were the UK's CVMP members during 1997/98 until Mrs Ashley-Smith resigned in July 1997 to take up a post as Head of Veterinary Sector in the EMEA. John O'Brien, VMD's Head of the Pharmaceuticals and Feed Additives team replaced Mrs Ashley-Smith on the CVMP. The CVMP's workload increased this year although the number of submissions through the centralised procedure was less

---

[18] Greater detail of the work carried out by the CVMP during 1997 can be found in the Third General Report on the Activities of the European Agency for the Evaluation of Medicinal Products 1997, available from the EMEA at 7 Westferry Circus, Canary Wharf, London E14 4HB.

than expected. The proposal to amend Council Regulation (EEC) 2309/93 to permit new substances in companion animals to be eligible for the centralised procedure is expected to lead to an increase in the number of applications in 1998. During 1997/98 the UK was rapporteur for four new MRL applications and two centralised applications. The main burden of the CVMP's work remains the establishment of MRLs for old substances and the UK shouldered a significant amount of this workload this year. First assessment of these applications was completed and, although much work remains to be done in dealing with the responses by applicants, this is expected to be completed by the new deadline of 1 January 2000.

VMD staff also attended meetings of the following CVMP working groups during the year:

– Safety of residues

– Quality Working Party

– Pharmacovigilance

– Antimicrobial Resistance

– Immunologicals Working Party

– Efficacy Working Group

– Standing Committee for veterinary pharmaceuticals

EMEA Management Board

Dr Michael Rutter was re-appointed at the beginning of 1997 as one of the two UK members of the **EMEA Management Board**. The Agency is now well established and recognised as a major partner in the international regulatory system. Details of its activities are published in its third General Report for 1997 available from the Agency.

Veterinary Mutual Recognition Facilitation Group

The Veterinary Mutual Recognition Facilitation Group held its first meeting in London in April 1997. This Group was set up by the UK at the invitation of the Netherlands during their EU Presidency. It aims to help to resolve the inevitable operational difficulties of the decentralised applications system. Mr Steve Dean, VMD's Director of Licensing, was appointed to act as Chairman to this Group to the end of the UK's EU Presidency in June 1998. As well as considering 19 applications under the mutual recognition procedures this year the Group adopted a Best Practice Guide and endorsed a list of ideal submission dates for applications to ensure adherence to the strict timetables.

EC working groups

EC working groups are involved in formulating many of the decisions which shape the EC legislation on veterinary medicines. VMD staff continued this year to represent the UK on the European Commission's **Veterinary Pharmaceutical Committee**, and its **Distribution Working Group**. They also represented the UK at meetings of the **Standing Committee on Veterinary Medicinal Products and the Standing Committee for Feedingstuffs**. Summary reports of these meeting are published in the Medicines Act Veterinary Information Service (MAVIS) (see Appendix D).

VMD staff also continued this year to assist in progressing the European Commission's IT initiative by chairing meetings of the **Eudratrack Working Group** and the **Joint Eudratrack Working Group** and attending meetings of the **Telematic Committee,** the **Eudranet Working Group** and the **Eudrawatch Working Group**. This initiative is aimed to provide and promote communication between the authorities of the member states, the Commission and the EMEA.

VMD staff also attended meetings this year of the **Notice to Applicants Working Group,** which agrees how applications for marketing authorisations should be submitted and processed. VMD staff provided the draft for a second volume to the Guidance Volume of the Notice to applicants on Procedural Matters which was passed to industry for comment in August 1997.

Working internationally

The VMD also actively participates in international discussions on a wide range of aspects of veterinary medicines.

Codex Alimentarius Commission

The Codex Alimentarius Commission (CAC) is a collection of internationally adopted food standards aimed at protecting consumers' health and ensuring fair practices in the food trade. At the 22nd Session of the Commission in Geneva on 23-28 June 1997, a proposal to adopt draft maximum residue limits for bovine somatotropin (BST) was suspended pending the re-evaluation of new scientific data by the **Joint Expert Committee on Food Additives (JECFA)** and **the Codex Committee on Veterinary Drug Residues in Food (CCRVDF)**, and the examination of the application of "other legitimate factors" in addition to sound scientific analysis, by the Committee on General Principles. The CCRVDF did not meet in 1997. The next session, the eleventh, will be held in Washington DC in September 1998. In preparation for the Washington meeting, the VMD submitted comments on a paper on the control of veterinary drug residues in milk and milk products to be considered at the eleventh session.

Veterinary International Co-operation on Harmonisation (VICH) Working Group on Ecotoxicity.

VMD staff represented the EU this year at the two meetings of the **Veterinary International Co-operation on Harmonisation (VICH) Working Group on Ecotoxicity.** Good progress was made by the Group in achieving harmonisation on Phase I guidance for ecotoxicity testing for veterinary medicinal products. Work will continue in 1998 with developing guidance on fate and effects testing.

Increasing public knowledge and understanding of veterinary medicines

Work continued this year to improve public awareness and understanding of the rigorous safeguards which ensure the safety, quality and efficacy of veterinary medicines on the UK market. We seek to do this through publishing relevant information to explain the controls, how we operate and our plans and results. We also ensure that we meet consumer representatives regularly to discuss the effects of our work.

Explaining the controls on veterinary medicines

The VMD publishes a series of guidance notes (Animal Medicines European Licensing Information and Advice (AMELIA) Guidance Notes) on various issues to assist the industry in their interpretation and application of European Legislation on veterinary medicines. This year we also issued a revised guidance note on marketing authorisations for the parallel import of veterinary medicines (AMELIA 9) and published a new guidance note on appeals procedures (AMELIA 15).[19]

Explaining how we operate

An updated booklet on "The Work of the Veterinary Medicines Directorate" was published in September 1997.[20] This describes how the VMD operates with the VPC and other Government Departments to safeguard public health, animal health and the environment and promote animal welfare.

Publishing our results and plans

The VMD issues a number of publications each year to inform readers about our work and general developments in the control of veterinary medicines. Appendix D to this report sets out full details of all of the publications issued this year. Many of these (and previous VMD publications) are now also available on the VMD's website.[21] This year we also established a VMD Publications Panel, chaired by the VMD Chief Executive, to oversee all of our publications. The panel's aims are to ensure that all VMD publications are clear, easy to understand and of the right quality.

Working with consumers

On 13 February 1998 we held our annual meeting with representatives from consumer organisations. Discussions included the links between VMD and the new Food Standards Agency, growth promoting hormones, antibiotic resistance and the VMD's post licensing surveillance work. A note of that meeting is available on request.[22]

---

[19] Copies of these guidance notes are available from VMD (telephone 01932 336911)
[20] Copies of this booklet are available from VMD (telephone 01932 336911)
[21] Web:http://www.open.gov.uk/vmd/vmdhome.htm
[22] Copies of these minutes are available from VMD (telephone 01932 36911)

Applying Citizen's Charter principles

Although the VMD's main customer is not the general public, we seek to ensure compliance with the principles of the Citizen's Charter for all of our activities and have incorporated them into our Customer Service Standards. We continue to assure our compliance with these standards and principles through close monitoring.

Adopting Customer Service Standards

The VMD aims to operate in accordance with the standards set out in the Customer Service Statement it published in 1994.[23] In addition from 1 April 1997 we formally adopted the following new standards announced by the then Government for all Government Departments and Agencies. (Although many were the same as those already in our Customer Service Statement):

"In serving you, every ..Government..Agency will aim to do the following:

1. Answer your letters quickly and clearly. (The VMD has a target to answer all letters within 15 working days of receipt.)

2. See you within 10 minutes of any appointments at its offices.

3. Provide clear and straightforward information about its services and report on the results.

4. Consult its regular users about the services it provides and report on the results.

5. Have at least one complaints procedure for the services it provides, and send you information about the procedure if you ask.

6. Do everything that is reasonably possible to make its services available to everyone, including people with special needs."

Assuring compliance

The most significant step taken this year to assure our compliance with these standards was the introduction of a computerised correspondence tracking system in February 1998. This monitors the speed with which all correspondence handled by VMD staff is answered (see standard 1 above). Other actions include:

● establishing the VMD Publications Panel (see page 35 of this report);

● conducting customer satisfaction consultations and holding regular meetings with industry and consumer representatives (see page 35 of this report);

● making our Customer Service Statement, including its complaints procedure, available on our website (see page 35 of this report); and

● ensuring that our new building has appropriate facilities for disabled staff and visitors (see page 28 of this report);.

[23] Copies of the VMD's Customer Service Statement are available from VMD (telephone 01932 336911)

Maintaining a highly motivated and skilled workforce

We are committed to maintaining a highly motivated and skilled workforce and promoting a climate which will encourage staff to develop their skills, fulfil their potential, enjoy their job and make a full contribution to the work of the Agency.[24] We seek to do this by selecting staff on their merit, investing in their training, listening to their views, encouraging their initiative, ensuring their health and safety and maintaining good industrial relations with their official representatives.

Selecting our staff

The VMD recruits on the basis of fair and open competition and selects its staff on merit. During the year we completed eight recruitment exercises. Of the 23 appointments made this year 15 chose to provide details of their ethnic origin and whether or not they were disabled.

Grade	White	Other Ethnic Group	Ethnic Group not Disclosed	Female	Disclosed Disability	Total	% Disclosed Non-white	% Female	% Disclosed Disability
AO	8	0	3	8	0	11	0.0	72.7	0.0
AA	2	1	3	4	0	6	16.6	66.7	0.0
EO	1	0	0	1	0	1	0.0	100	0.0
PO 1	1	0	0	0	0	1	0.0	0.0	0.0
VA	1	0	0	1	0	1	0.0	100	0.0
VRO	1	0	2	1	0	3	0.0	33.3	0.0
Total	14	1	8	15	0	23	4.3	65.2	0.0

Investing in training

The VMD is committed to providing the training our staff need to do their job effectively. We encourage staff development through programmes of job related training and attendance at national and scientific meetings. All staff, including temporary staff, attend an induction course within three months of joining.

Investors in People

In March 1997 the VMD undertook to achieve **Investors in People (IIP)** accreditation by 31 March 1999. This is a national initiative designed to ensure that staff are trained to meet the needs of the business. Surrey Training and Enterprise Council (TEC) are providing advice on our development. After a series of introductory seminars we held a lunchtime barbecue for all VMD staff on 5 June to launch this initiative. During the year we also took the following actions which will assist in our achievement of IIP standard:

- Personal Development Plans were introduced to help staff identify and prioritise their training needs;

[24] This commitment is described more detail in the VMD's People Strategy, set out at Appendix E.

- a new system was developed for evaluating the effectiveness of training undertaken by staff;

- a formal training plan was included in the VMD's Five Year Corporate Plan for 1998/99-2002/03;

- quarterly "Achievements and Progress" notices were published;

- a strategic planning workshop was held on "Communications";

- a statement of VMD's aims was introduced as part of its new logo; and

- a computerised training database was established.

Listening to staff

Staff attitude survey

On 2 January we announced our intention to conduct a comprehensive **survey of staff attitudes** to working at the VMD. The benefits of holding such a survey had become clear from strategic seminars and from the benchmarking exercise (see page 14) which had revealed the need to encourage more and better upward communication from staff to management. Questionnaires were issued to all staff in March 1998.

Encouraging initiative

Staff Suggestions Scheme

To try to harness the initiative and imagination of our staff in improving their working arrangements, environment and service to customers, the VMD runs its own **Staff Suggestions Scheme.** This year we received thirty suggestions under this scheme. Eleven of these were successfully adopted and implemented.

Ensuring Health and Safety

As part of our commitment to ensuring the health, safety and welfare of our employees, this year we have provided health and safety training for staff in first aid at work, fire safety awareness, risk assessment and safe lifting and carrying. We have also undertaken eyesight testing for staff using VDUs and provided corrective lenses where needed. Staff were also asked to complete risk assessments relating to their use of VDUs and where remedial action was identified this was taken.

Maintaining good industrial relations

Regular and frank communication with staff representatives is the cornerstone to good industrial relations at the VMD. We held four formal meetings during the year to discuss issues raised by the Trade Union Side. Between these meetings we had a number of other informal discussions on specific topics as the need arose. Such meetings were called by both parties and, despite busy schedules, all those involved made themselves available and we continued to enjoy a positive approach to the discussions this year.

Looking forward

Our targets for 1998/99

The Minister of Agriculture, Fisheries and Food announced to Parliament the following "high level" targets for the VMD for 1998/99 on 30th April 1998.

Safety and Quality

● To enter Serious Adverse Reaction Surveillance Scheme (SARSS) reports onto the database as follows:

Human reports	within 2 working days
Serious animal reports	within 2 working days
Non-serious animal reports	within 10 working days

● Report to the Veterinary Products Committee (VPC) each quarter reviewing trends in SAR reports and identifying areas requiring evaluation.

● To collect and analyse 95% of the samples in the national residues surveillance plan.

● To provide high quality policy advice to Ministers.

● To provide high quality scientific assessment work.

Standards of Service

● 100% compliance with timetables for Centralised and Decentralised authorisation procedures (including Maximum Residue Limits).

● 90% of New Marketing Authorisations to be determined or referred to VPC within 120 clock days.

● 100% of New Marketing Authorisations to be determined within 210 clock days.

● 100% of valid variation applications to have first assessment by 75 clock days and to be determined by 150 clock days.

● 100% of valid renewal applications to have first assessment by 90 clock days and to be determined by 180 clock days.

People

● Achieve Investors in People accreditation by 31 March 1999.

Financial Control

● To recover from industry and Government the full economic cost of each of its main business activities of:

– licensing and surveillance

– policy work

– residue monitoring.

● To operate within the net cash allocations agreed for the VMD by MAFF's Management Board.

Links with Food Standards Agency

The White Paper "The Foods Standards Agency: a Force for Change", published in January 1998, set out the Government's proposals for a Food Standards Agency (FSA). The Government proposes to introduce a number of mechanisms to enable the FSA to ensure that proper account is taken of food safety considerations in the licensing of veterinary medicines. The VMD will work closely with staff of the future FSA during 1998/99 on preparations for the Agency's launch.

Changes in licensing procedures

Since 1 January 1998 marketing authorisation holders cannot apply for a national authorisation for a product which is already authorised within the European Union. All such applications will now be dealt with under the decentralised procedure. Although this change will inevitably lead to many procedural changes and changes to the scope of authorisations, the basic requirement to demonstrate the safety, quality and efficacy of the product will remain.

Changes to the VPC

In accordance with the Government's wish to see greater openness in the development and execution of food safety policy, the membership of the Veterinary Products Committee is being increased through the appointment of two lay members. The scope of advice available to the VPC is also being widened through the appointment to it of a person with expertise in the area of occupational health/hygiene. A consultation exercise was started in July 1997 inviting nominations for these three positions as well as for the 11 members of the Committee whose terms of office expired on 31 December 1997. The new appointees took up their positions with effect from 1 May 1998.

Advances in IT and the next millennium

As part of the continuing development of VMD IT systems, the following developments are planned for the period 1998/2000:

- ongoing millennium compliance programme including adopting Microsoft Exchange/Outlook for E-mail and Office 97 for the desktop;

- implementation of the new VMD Electronic Document and Image Management System (EDIMS);

- re-development of all VMD Licensing systems and integration with Workflow and EDIMS;

- integration of the Pharmacovigilance system with EDIMS;

- integration of Residues Surveillance systems with Laboratory Information Management systems;

- extension of the existing Statutory Residues Surveillance system to include follow up investigation requirements;

- incorporation of Records Management and Correspondence Management systems into the VMD EDIMS;

- use of the VMD EDIMS to dynamically publish VMD documents on the VMD Web Site;

- implementation of a VMD Intranet; and

- provision of remote access for VMD customers to Licence Applications.

Appendices

Appendix A

Veterinary Medicines Directorate Ownership Board

The Ownership Board has two primary rôles:

a) an advisory rôle to or on behalf of the Minister, and b) to provide advice, support and assistance to the Chief Executive as and when he may request it. In carrying out (a) above the Board will provide the Minister with the necessary information and strategic advice to allow the setting of challenging, but realistic, targets following consideration of:

- VMD's Corporate and Business plans, its current performance targets and its Annual Report and Accounts; and

- VMD's performance and the need for any corrective action.

The Board will also advise on:

- any unresolved disagreement between the VMD and the department as customer and any significant unresolved problems referred to it by the Minister, Agency or Department concerning the relationship between the VMD and its external customers; and

- the interpretation of the Framework Document.

The Chairman and members of the Ownership Board are appointed by the Minister.

Membership at 31 March 1998

Chairman

Mr R J D Carden CB	Deputy Secretary
	(Food Safety and Enviroment Directorate) MAFF

Members

Mr P Elliott	Principal Finance Officer, MAFF
Mr B H B Dickinson	Head of Animal Health Group, MAFF
Dr J M Rutter	Director and Chief Executive, VMD
Dr E Smales	Department of Health
Professor I D Aitken OBE	Independent Member
Mr A H Simon OBE	Independent Member

Secretary

Mr C Southgate	Financial Management Division, MAFF

Appendix B

Advisory Committees
Veterinary Products Committee

The Veterinary Products Committee (VPC) was established in 1970 under Section 4 of the Medicines Act 1968 to:

- give advice with respect to safety, quality and efficacy in relation to the veterinary use of any substance or article (not being an instrument, apparatus or appliance) to which any provision of the Medicines Act is applicable; and

- promote the collection of information relating to suspected adverse reactions for the purpose of enabling such advice to be given.

These terms of reference have been extended to include veterinary medicinal products to which relevant EC legislation applies and which come before the Committee for consideration.

Membership at 31 March 1998

Chairman
Prof. I D Aitken OBE, BVMS, PhD, DVM&S (hc), FRAgS, CBiol, FIBiol, MRCVS
Scientific Director, Edinburgh Centre for Rural Research

Members
Dr D N Bateman BSc, MB BS, MRCS, MD, FRCP
Medical Director, Northern & Yorkshire Regional Drug & Therapeutics Centre, University of Newcastle-upon-Tyne

Prof. P M Biggs CBE, DSc, Dr hc(Liege), DVM hc(Munich), FRCPath, CBiol, FIBiol, FRCVS, FRS *Visiting Professor in Microbiology at the Royal Veterinary College, London*

Prof. J W Bridges DSc, PhD, MRCPath, CChem, FRSC, CBiol, FIBiol, MInstEnvSci, FIOSH, *Director, European Institute of Health and Medical Science, Guildford, Surrey*

Prof. J R Brown BSc, MSc, PhD, FRPharmS, CChem, FRSC, CBiol, FIBiol
Deputy Chief Executive and Pro Vice Chancellor, University of Sunderland

Mr D S Collins MVB, CBiol, MIBiol, DVPH (MH), MRCVS

Practising Veterinary Surgeon, Consultant in Veterinary Public Health, Belfast

Dr A Cooke BSc, PhD, CBiol, MIBiol

Environmental Impacts Team, English Nature, Peterborough

Dr R Gaskell BVSc, PhD, MRCVS

Department of Veterinary Pathology, University of Liverpool

Prof. G Gettinby BSc, PhD, CStat

Department of Statistics and Modelling Science, University of Strathclyde

Prof. C A Hart PhD, BSc, MB BS, FRCP

Professor of Medical Microbiology and Genito-Urinary Medicine, University of Liverpool

Dr R J Heitzman BSc, PhD

Private Consultant working for FAO/WHO, EU

Dr M H Jepson BPharm, MSc, PhD, FRPharmS, MInstPkg, MIInfSc, MCPP

Department of Pharmaceutical and Biological Sciences, Aston University

Prof. P Lees CBE, BPharm, PhD, Hon Assoc RCVS, CBiol, FIBiol, Dr hc(Gent)
Vice Principal, Royal Veterinary College, University of London

Prof. K A Linklater BVMS, PhD, CBiol, FIBiol, FRAgS, FRCVS

Director of Scottish Agricultural Colleges Veterinary Services, Edinburgh

Prof. Q McKellar BVMS, PhD, MRCVS

Currently Head of Department of Veterinary Pharmacology, University of Glasgow
Director Moredun Research Institute, Edinburgh

Dr C J Powell BSc, MSc, PhD, DipRCPath, FRCPath
Reader in Pharmaceutical & Chemical Safety, St. Bartholomew's and Royal London School of Medicine and Dentistry, London

Prof. R H Richards BA, MA, Veterinary MB, PhD, MRCVS
Director, Institute of Aquaculture, University of Stirling

Mr D Skilton BVSc, MRCVS
Practising Veterinary Surgeon, Cheadle Hulme, Cheshire

Mr R A Wickham BVetMed, MRCVS
Practising Veterinary Surgeon, Canterbury, Kent

Dr D F Wishart DVM, BVMS, MRCVS, MIBiol
Private Consultant

Medical and Scientific Panel

The Medical and Scientific Panel was established in 1991 as a sub-Committee to the VPC to:

- evaluate research currently available, and in progress, on organophosphorus (OP) sheep dip products in relation to possible human exposure;

- advise on any additional work that may be needed to elucidate the potential long term effects on human of OP sheep dip;

- advise on the suitability of any projects submitted for research; and

- report its findings to the Veterinary Products Committee, as its sub-committee.

Membership at 31 March 1998

Chairman

Dr D N Bateman BSc, MB BS, MRCS, MD, FRCP

Medical Director, Northern & Yorkshire Regional Drug & Therapeutics Centre, University of Newcastle-upon-Tyne

Members

Dr R W Brimblecombe PhD, DSc, FRCPath, FIBiol

Independent Consultant in Pharmaceutical Research and Development.

Professor S J W Evans BA, MSc, FSS, FIS, Hon MFPHM, Hon MRCR

Visiting Professor of Medical Statistics, London School of Hygiene & Tropical Medicine
Senior Epidemiologist, Medicines Control Agency, London.

Professor J B Harris BPharm, PhD, MRPharmS, FIBiol, CBiol

Head of School and Professor of Experimental Neurology, University of Newcastle-upon-Tyne.

Dr M K Johnson PhD, BSc, ARCS

Independent Consultant in Toxicology

Professor M H Lader OBE, DSc, PhD, MD, FRCPsych

Professor of Clinical Psychopharmacology, Institute of Psychiatry, University of London

Dr T C Marrs MD, DSc, FRCPath, DipRCPath (Tox), FIBiol
Senior Medical Officer, Department of Health, London

Professor K McPherson BA, MD, PhD
Professor of Public Health Epidemiology, Department of Public Health and Policy,
London School of Hygiene and Tropical Medicine

Dr R G Rawbone MB BS, MD, LRCP, MRCS
Senior Employment Medical Adviser, Head of Medical Unit Health Directorate,
Health and Safety Executive

Professor E M Sedgwick BSc, MB ChB, MRCP, FRCP
Professor of Clinical Neurophysiology, University of Southampton

Professor P K Thomas CBE, MB BS, DSc, MD, FRCP, FRCPath
Emeritus Professor of Neurology, Royal Free Hospital School of Medicine,
University of London

Appraisal Panel on Human Suspected Adverse Reactions

The Appraisal Panel on Human Suspected Adverse Reactions was established in November 1991 to:

- evaluate all suspected adverse reactions to veterinary medicinal products in humans to:

    i) identify any trends and signals of emergent problems

    ii) generate hypotheses as to possible causes of these trends;

- monitor the consequences of recommendations for changes in working practices or use;

- report its findings to the Veterinary Products Committee; and

- produce an Annual Report of its findings.

Membership at 31 March 1998

Chairman

Dr C Powell

St Bartholomew's and the Royal London School of Medicines and Dentistry

Assessors

Mr A Spence	*Health and Safety Executive*
Dr T Marrs	*Department of Health*
Mr D Renshaw	*Department of Health*
Dr R Rawbone	*Health and Safety Executive*

Independent Expert Members

Ms L Bowen	*Veterinary Medicine*
Professor G Dunn	*Epidemiology*
Dr J Fowler	*Toxicology*
Professor J Henry	*Clinical Toxicology*
Dr D Ray	*Neurotoxicology*
Dr I White	*Dermatology*

Secretary

Mrs C Evans	*VMD*

Advisory Group on Veterinary Residues

The Advisory Group on Veterinary Residues was established in 1995 to:

- advise on the incidence and concentrations of residues of veterinary medicines in samples collected under both the statutory and non-statutory surveillance programmes;

- assess and advise on the scope and operation of the statutory veterinary surveillance programme to ensure its continued compliance with the requirements of the European Community legislation;

- advise, with particular reference to food safety, on the non-statutory residues surveillance programmes and consider the need for further non-statutory analytical surveys;

- advise on the current and future research strategies and objectives in the light of current and potential problems associated with the presence of veterinary residues in food from food producing species;

- set up expert panels as necessary to consider and advise on the work and objectives of the Advisory Group and the R&D requirements;

- prepare an Annual Report on Veterinary Residue Surveillance; report annually to the Veterinary Products Committee and the Steering Group on Chemical Aspects of Food Surveillance; and publish as soon as possible, interim results of surveys and monitoring activities in such form as is appropriate.

Membership at 31 March 1998

Chairman

Dr J M Rutter, VMD Chief Executive

Members

Mrs D Craig MBE	Independent Member-Expertise in consumer matters
Dr R Heitzman	Independent Member-Expertise in analytical matters
Dr H Cook	National Farmers' Union
Mr G French	British Retail Consortium
Dr K Lawrence	National Office of Animal Health Ltd.
Mr R M Stevenson	British Veterinary Association

Dr B Vernon	UKASTA
Ms L Morris	Department of Health/MAFF Joint Food Standards and Safety Group
D J Collins	Department of Health/MAFF Joint Food Standards and Safety Group
Dr D Atkins	Department of Health/MAFF Joint Food Standards and Safety Group
Dr G Kennedy	Department of Agriculture for Northern Ireland, Veterinary Science
Mr R Huey	Department of Agriculture for Northern Ireland, Veterinary Service
Mr D W Renshaw	Department of Health/MAFF Joint Food Standards and Safety Group

Secretariat (all from VMD)

Mr C Penny

Dr J F Kay

Mr D J Lewsey

Mrs J E Gill

Appendix C

Summary of applications received

	1995/96	1996/97	1997/98
Applications			
Decentralised UK RMS *	-	10	13
Decentralised UK CMS **	-	8	1
Major	11	14	14
Complex	16	20	25
Standard	32	30	61
Simple	67	57	102
Provisional (Major and Complex)	6	1	5
Emergency Vaccines	15	13	17
Variations			
Decentralised UK RMS	-	6	3
Decentralised UK CMS	-	7	14
Complex	25	21	16
Standard	584	612	305
Administrative	310	420	768
Emergency Vaccines	21	7	
Renewals			
Marketing Authorisations	154	243	230
Emergency Vaccines	30	20	26
Transfers	65	7	19
Animal Test Certificates			
Applications	3	29	44
Variations	34	25	22
Renewals	14	11	11
Animal Test Exemption Scheme			
Applications	24	15	-
Variations	23	14	2
Renewals	13	6	

* reference member state

** concerned member state

	1995/96	1996/97	1997/98
Manufacturers Licences			
Applications	5	1	3
Variations	19	9	23
Annual Fees	40	26	43
Wholesale Dealers Licences			
Applications	17	7	4
Variations	22	9	23
Annual Fees	190	138	195
Inspections by MCA			
Super	2	-	-
Major	2	1	3
Standard	7	8	8
Minor	24	18	25
Wholesale Dealer	25	26	36
Other			
Inspections by VMD (excluding QA/QC)	16	7	10
Export Certificates	2247	1191	1681

Performance Targets 1997/98

The VMD's performance against targets are set out below.

TARGET :- To determine 80% of new Marketing Authorisation applications within 120 clock days; 95% within 200 clock days.

		1995/96	1996/97	1997/98
Target	% within 120 clock days	77	80	80
	% within 200 clock days	95	95	95
Achieved	% within 120 clock days	97	82	87
	% within 200 clock days	98	99	96
Licences determined		116	92	150

TARGET :- To ensure that the first assessment of variations outstanding for more than 75 clock days on 1 April is completed by 31 October 1997.
To ensure that the first assessment of renewals (including Transfers) outstanding for more than 90 clock days is completed by 31 December 1997.

No. of Variations outstanding for more than 75 clock days	312
No. of outstanding Variations received prior to 1 April 1997	510
No. of initial assessments completed by 31 October 1997.	510

No. of Renewals outstanding for more than 75 clock days	191
No. of outstanding Renewals received prior to 1 April 1997	260
No. of initial assessments completed by 31 October 1997.	260

TARGET :- To ensure that first assessments for Variations and Renewals (including Transfers) are completed within 75 and 90 clock days respectively.

No. of Variations received since 31 March 1997	1039	
No. with initial assessment completed within 75 clock days.	978	94%
No. with initial assessment completed outside of target.	29	3%
No. of Variations received awaiting initial assessment.*	32	3%

No. of Renewals received since 31 March 1997	231	
No. with initial assessment completed within 90 clock days.	153	66%
No. with initial assessment completed outside of target.	46	20%
No. of Renewals received awaiting initial assessment.*	32	14%

Note - Relates to applications received in late February and in March 1998 which had not had an initial assessment completed by 31 March 1998.

TARGET :-   To recover from industry and Government the full economic cost of each of its main business activities of licensing and surveillance, policy work and residue monitoring.

Results for 1997/98	**Licensing and Surveillance Business**	**Policy Business**	**Residue Business**
	£'000	**£'000**	**£'000**
Income	3,360	1,584	3,837
Expenditure	3,354	1,562	3,375
Results +/(-)	6	22	162
% Cost recovery	100.2	101.4	104.4

Results for previous years % Cost recovery			
1996/97	103.5	102.8	101.4
1995/96	101.8	96.7	100.6

Appendix D

VMD publications and Statutory Instruments

Publications 1997/98 [25]

Veterinary Medicines Directorate Annual Report and Accounts 1996/97

Veterinary Medicines Directorate Five Year Corporate Plan 1998/99-2002/03

Annual Report on Surveillance for Veterinary Residues in 1996

The 1996 Report of the Appraisal Panel for Human Suspected Adverse Reactions to Veterinary Medicinal Products

Animal Medicines European Licensing Information and Advice (AMELIA)

Guidance Notes:

14. The Registration of Homoeopathic Veterinary Products Scheme-Guidance for manufacturers, importers and suppliers

14a. The Registration of Homoeopathic Veterinary Products Scheme-Guidance for manufacturers, importers and suppliers-Control and Quality of Homoeopathic stocks

14 b The Registration of Homoeopathic Veterinary Products Scheme-Guidance for manufacturers, importers and suppliers-The Manufacture and Control of dosage forms

14c. The Registration of Homoeopathic Veterinary Products Scheme-Guidance for manufacturers, importers and suppliers-Fees

15. Appeals Procedure for Applications for marketing authorisations for veterinary medicinal products

Medicines Act Veterinary Information Service (MAVIS) newsletter-Issues 22-25

Scientific Papers

Details of scientific papers published by VMD staff are published in the MAVIS newsletter.

[25] Copies of these publications are available from VMD (telephone 01932 336911).

Statutory Instruments coming into effect in 1997/98

SI 1997 No.638

The Medicines (Medicated Animal Feeding Stuffs) (Amendment) Regulations 1997

Made:	5 March 1997
Laid before Parliament:	6 March 1997
Coming into force:	1 April 1997

SI 1997 No.1349

The Medicines (Registered Homoeopathic Veterinary Medicinal Products) (General Sale List) Order 1997

Made:	23 May 1997
Coming into force:	30 June 1997

SI 1997 No.1350

The Medicines (Pharmacy and General Sale-Exemption) (Amendment) Order 1997

Made:	23 May 1997
Laid before Parliament:	9 June 1997
Coming into force:	30 June 1997

SI 1997 No.1469

The Medicines (Products for Animal Use-Fees) Regulations 1997

Made:	9 June 1997
Laid before Parliament:	10 June 1997
Coming into force:	1 July 1997

SI 1997 No.1727

The Medicines (Stilbenes and Thyrostatic Substances Prohibition) (Revocation) Order 1997

Made:	18 July 1997
Laid before Parliament:	21 July 1997
Coming into force:	11 August 1997

SI 1997 No.1728

The Medicines (Control of Substances for Manufacture) (Revocation) Order 1997

Made:	18 July 1997
Laid before Parliament:	21 July 1997
Coming into force:	11 August 1997

SI 1729 No.1729   **The Animals and Animal Products (Examination for Residues and Maximum Residue Limits) Regulations 1997**

Made:	18 July 1997
Coming into force:	11 August 1997

SI 1997 No.2884   **The Medicines (Restrictions on the Administration of Veterinary Medicinal Products) Amendment Regulations 1997**

Made:	4 December 1997
Laid before Parliament:	8 December 1997
Coming into force:	1 February 1998

SI 1997 No.2892   **The Medicines (Veterinary Drugs) (Pharmacy and Merchants' List) (Amendment) Order 1997**

Made:	8 December 1997
Laid before Parliament:	9 December 1997
Coming into force:	1 January 1998

SI 1997 No.2893   **The Charges for Inspections and Controls Regulations 1997**

Made:	8 December 1997
Coming into force:	1 January 1998

Appendix E

VMD people strategy – Our commitment to staff

All managers will promote a climate within VMD which will encourage staff to develop their skills, fulfil their potential, enjoy their job and make a full contribution to the work of the Agency. In particular we shall:

Tools and environment

- provide a place to work which is safe and pleasant to work in and without risk to health;

- provide the tools staff need to do their job;

Training and Opportunity

- provide equal opportunities for all;

- provide the necessary training;

Support and Encouragement

- keep staff informed on all matters affecting them and listen to their views, concerns and suggestions for improvement;

- encourage staff to become involved in making decisions and delegate decision making to the lowest practicable level;

- provide a supportive climate to help plan and develop a career and give practical help where it is needed;

- give appropriate and timely feedback on performance and support efforts to improve should performance not be up to standard;

Recognition and reward

- ensure that the Staff Appraisal System and other personnel procedures are fairly applied throughout the VMD;

- recognise and acknowledge good performance and make full use of the methods available to reward it;

Corporate

- encourage initiatives to improve the image of the VMD; and

- maintain good industrial relations.

This will not be easy to achieve, but we are committed to making progress in all of these areas. We will consult staff on the working of this strategy regularly and incorporate suggestions for improvements in later versions.

The Veterinary Medicines Directorate

Accounts 1997/98

The Veterinary Medicines Directorate

An Executive Agency of the Ministry of Agriculture, Fisheries and Food

Accounts 1997/98

Foreword to the Accounts for the year ended 31 March 1998
BACKGROUND INFORMATION

1.   The Veterinary Medicines Directorate (VMD) was formed in April 1989. It was established as an Executive Agency under the Government's "Next Steps" initiative on 2 April 1990.

2.   The VMD's responsibilities include the authorisation of veterinary medicines and post-authorisation surveillance of suspected adverse reactions, the monitoring of residues in meat and animal products, the provision of policy advice to Ministers and management of the Ministry's research and development programme for veterinary medicines aimed at safeguarding public and animal health.

3.   The VMD's costs are financed through payment of fees by the veterinary pharmaceutical industry for veterinary medicines authorisation, and by the slaughterhouse industry for statutory residues monitoring. The costs of policy advice, non-statutory residues monitoring and R & D are financed wholly by the Ministry.

4.   The Directorate is required to achieve full cost recovery across the three business areas of licensing, residues and policy work whilst at the same time improving its cost efficiency and service delivery. Improvements in the quality of customer service are being pursued in line with the Citizen's Charter.

5.   Certain elements of the work for which the VMD is responsible are sub-contracted to other Government Agencies. These include the Veterinary Laboratories Agency, the Central Science Laboratory, the Medicines Control Agency and the Meat Hygiene Service.

Principal Activities

6.   Under the provisions of EC and UK legislation, no veterinary medicinal product may be marketed without a product licence or marketing authorisation, which is granted only after the product has undergone a detailed scientific assessment of its safety, quality and efficacy. Once a product has been authorised, post authorisation surveillance is co-ordinated by the VMD. The National Surveillance Scheme is a statutory scheme under which random samples from farms and slaughterhouses are examined for the presence of residues of veterinary medicines. The non-statutory residues surveillance programme supplements the statutory scheme by examining samples of home-produced and imported meat and animal products purchased from retail and other outlets. The Suspected Adverse Reaction Surveillance Scheme monitors and responds to reports of suspected adverse reactions to veterinary medicines in both humans and animals.

7. The VMD provides policy advice to Ministers on all aspects of the licensing and use of veterinary medicines, and manages the Ministry's R & D programme on veterinary medicines.

Preparation of Accounts

8. The accounts have been prepared in accordance with a Treasury Direction dated 18 February 1992 in pursuance of Section 5 of the Exchequer and Audit Departments Act 1921.

9. The VMD is Vote financed through the Ministry of Agriculture, Fisheries and Food (MAFF). This means that income and most expenditure are monitored under a net control total by H M Treasury.

Results

10. The income and expenditure account shows a surplus of £191,000 in the year to 31 March 1998.

Review of Activities

11. The main events which took place during the year are reported more fully in the Annual Report. Events relevant to the Accounts included:

● Benchmarking the VMD's activities against the European Business Excellence Model and Customer Satisfaction Surveys of each VMD business.

● The extension of industry funded residues surveillance to cover poultry, fish, eggs, milk and farmed game from 1 January 1998. This should increase the VMD's residues income by about 61% in 1998/99.

● A 27% increase in the volume of licensing work received.

● The end of the transitional period for new European licensing arrangements which became compulsory on 1 January 1998.

● The start of construction of VMD's new £3.5m office block.

Fixed Assets

12. Investment in fixed assets has continued as the VMD improves its business and financial information. Fixed assets include IT equipment, office equipment, fixtures and fittings. The capitalisation threshold is £500 for capital assets. Buildings occupied by the VMD are owned by the Crown. An accommodation charge is paid to MAFF.

Research and Development

13.   Research and development is managed by the VMD with the aim of improving public safety and animal health and welfare. This work is dealt with more fully elsewhere in the Annual Report.

Future Developments

14.   The following developments during 1998/99 could affect the VMD's future operations:

● The continued development of the harmonised licensing arrangements across the Community which became obligatory on 1 January 1998.

● The completion of new office accommodation for the VMD at New Haw.

● The introduction of capital charging.

● The further refinement of customer/contractor relationships between the VMD and other parts of MAFF and Government setting up Memoranda of Understanding aimed at improving efficiency and raising standards.

● The establishment of the new Food Standards Agency.

● The extension of the statutory residues surveillance programme to include poultry, milk, eggs, fish and farmed game.

● The enhancement of the VMD training strategy as the VMD seeks to achieve IIP accreditation.

Events since the end of the Financial Year

15.   There have been no significant events.

Ownership Board

16.   The responsibility for advising the Minister on the VMD's targets, performance and management is exercised through an Ownership Board. The composition and terms of reference of the Ownership Board are set out in Appendix A to the Annual Report.

Management Group

17. The VMD's Management Group meets every two months to consider the Agency's management reports and draft plans. The Group is chaired by the Chief Executive. The Chief Executive, the Directors of Licensing and Policy and the VMD Secretary and Head of Business Unit meet weekly to discuss current matters.

Disabled Persons

18. The VMD complies with Equal Opportunities Legislation and MAFF policy in relation to disabled employees. Special facilities are provided where necessary.

Equal Opportunities and Health and Safety at Work

19. The VMD, as an Executive Agency of MAFF, applies the Ministry's policies on equal opportunities and health and safety at work. The VMD Secretary and Head of Business Unit is designated Equal Opportunities Officer for the Directorate.

Employee Involvement

20. The VMD encourages staff involvement in the day to day running of its activities through normal line management contacts. A staff suggestions scheme exists to encourage original ideas. Regular office notices and a 'New Building' newsletter are used to disseminate information. An annual staff meeting to review the work of the past year and discuss future plans is addressed by the Chief Executive and Directors. Staff have access to the staff welfare facilities offered by MAFF and Trade Union membership and representation is in accordance with departmental policies.

21. Investors in People and new building accommodation working groups have been set up to facilitate greater staff involvement in these projects.

J M RUTTER
Chief Executive and Agency Accounting Officer
7 July 1998

Veterinary Medicines Directorate

Income and Expenditure Account for the year ended 31 March 1998

NOTES		1998 £'000	1998 £'000	1997 £'000	1997 £'000
	INCOME				
2	Income from activities	**8,781**		8,460	
3	Less - Direct subcontracting costs	**(3,331)**		(3,426)	
	Net Income		**5,450**		5,034
	OPERATING UNIT EXPENDITURE				
4	Staff costs	**(2,966)**		(2,883)	
8	Depreciation	**(202)**		(182)	
5	Other operating costs	**(1,261)**		(1,056)	
	V.M.D. operating costs for year		**(4,429)**		(4,121)
	Operating result before departmental charges and other costs		**1,021**		913
	DEPARTMENTAL CHARGES AND OTHER COSTS				
	Overhead recharges	**(680)**		(568)	
	Veterinary Products Committee	**(82)**		(71)	
			(762)		(639)
	Operating surplus before interest on capital		**259**		274
7	Interest on capital		**(68)**		(71)
	Operating surplus for the year		**191**		203
	Operating surplus brought forward		**228**		25
	Operating surplus for the year		**191**		203
12	**Operating surplus carried forward**		**419**		228

The Income and Expenditure Account, which is prepared on an historical cost basis, reflects the total recognised gains or losses incurred by the Agency for the period to 31 March 1998. All activities arise from continuing operations.

The notes on pages 72 to 81 form part of these accounts

Veterinary Medicines Directorate

Balance Sheet as at 31 March 1998

NOTES		1998 £'000	1998 £'000	1997 £'000	1997 £'000
	Fixed assets				
8	Tangible assets		670		588
	Current assets				
9	Debtors and prepayments	1,356		796	
10	Cash at bank	34		43	
		1,390		839	
	Creditors: amounts falling due wtihin one year				
11	Creditors and income prepayments	(652)		(350)	
	Net current assets		738		489
	Total assets less current liabilities		1,408		1,077
	Financed by				
12	General fund		1,408		1,077

J M RUTTER
Chief Executive and
Agency Accounting Officer
7 July 1998

Veterinary Medicines Directorate

Cash Flow Statement for the year ended 31 March 1998

	1998	1997
	£'000	£'000
Net cash inflow from operating activities	911	1,468
Capital Expenditure and financial investment	(291)	(319)
Cash inflow before management of liquid resources and financing	620	1,149
Financing		
Total cash surplus paid to MAFF	(629)	(1,170)
Decrease in cash in the period	(9)	(21)

Note 1 to the Cash Flow Statement

Reconciliation of operating surplus to net cash inflow from operating activities

	1998		1997	
	£'000	£'000	£'000	£'000
Operating activities:				
Operating surplus for the year	191		203	
Depreciation	202		182	
MAFF overheads	680		568	
Other notional charges added back	92		96	
Other movements	(1)		1	
(Increase)/Decrease in debtors and prepayments	(560)		282	
Increase in creditors	307		136	
Net cash inflow from operating activities		911		1,468

The notes on pages 72 to 81 form part of these accounts

Note 2 to the Cash Flow Statement

Reconciliation to the appropriation accounts

The MAFF appropriation accounts report to Parliament the receipts and payments of the VMD as follows:

	Class III Vote 2 1998		Class III Vote 2 1997	
	£'000	£'000	£'000	£'000
Appropriations in aid	**5,777**		5,601	
Add: received from MAFF	**2,688**		3,144	
Total Agency Income		**8,465**		8,745
Less				
Total Running cost expenditure:				
Administrative excluding superannuation	**(3,733)**		(3,455)	
Subcontracted activities	**(3,378)**		(3,409)	
Veterinary Products Committee	**(84)**		(71)	
Superannuation contributions	**(359)**		(346)	
	(7,554)		(7,281)	
Capital expenditure	**(291)**		(315)	
		(7,845)		(7,596)
Total net Vote surplus		**620**		1,149
Movement in funds held in the VMD local bank account, pending transfer to MAFF		**9**		21
Total cash surplus paid to MAFF		**629**		1,170

Veterinary Medicines Directorate

Notes to the Accounts

1. ACCOUNTING POLICIES

a) **Accounting Conventions**

The accounts have been prepared under the Historic Cost Convention modified by the inclusion of fixed assets at their value to the business by reference to current costs. Without limiting the information given, the accounts meet the accounting and disclosure requirements of the Companies Act and the Accounting Standards issued or adopted by the Accounting Standards Board so far as those requirements are appropriate.

b) **Depreciation**

Assets costing £500 or more are capitalised and are depreciated to a nominal residual value over their estimated useful lives as follows:

Computer equipment and software	4 years
Office equipment	10 years
Furniture and fittings	10 years

Fixed Assets are included on the face of the Balance Sheet at their value to the business.

c) **VAT**

Input VAT is charged to the Income and Expenditure Account in the year in which it is incurred.

d) **Overheads**

Central Ministry of Agriculture, Fisheries and Food overheads are charged on a notional basis and included in the accounts. These include charges for central services such as Establishments, Information Division, Office Services, Legal Services and Finance.

Other site overheads such as security are paid direct to the Veterinary Laboratories Agency.

e) **Income Prepayments**

An adjustment to income has been made to reflect income prepayments at the year end. This represents that portion of the fee received for major, complex and standard marketing authorisations which had not been determined at the year end.

f) **Recovery from Government Funds**

From 1 April 1991 the VMD took over responsibility for managing the research and development programme on veterinary medicines. These costs do not form part of the cost recovery targets and are not borne by industry.

2. INCOME

	1998	1997
a) *Income from Activities*	£'000	£'000
Income was earned from the following activities:		
Licensing	3,360	3,194
Statutory Residues Testing	2,836	2,611
Non-Statutory Residues Surveillance	1,001	1,109
Policy	1,584	1,546
	8,781	8,460

b) *Key Performance Target*

The VMD had been set one key financial performance target in 1997/98 as follows:

Full cost recovery for each of the business activities of licensing, policy work and residues monitoring.

Results:

An overall cost recovery of 102.2% was achieved. Cost recovery performance within each of the VMD principal business areas was as follows:

Licensing	1998 £'000	1997 £'000
Income	3,360	3,194
Staff Costs	(1,921)	(1,825)
Depreciation	(131)	(115)
Subcontracting Costs	(155)	(154)
Other Costs	(1,147)	(992)
Total income less costs (cost recovery = 100.2%)	6	108

Residues	1998 £'000	1997 £'000
Statutory Scheme		
Income	2,836**	2,611*
Staff Costs	(186)	(98)
Depreciation	(13)	(6)
Testing and Collection Costs	(2,312)	(2,326)
Other Costs	(179)	(155)
Total income less costs (cost recovery = 105.4%)	146	26

*   Including £350,000 received from MAFF out of negotiated BSE funding relating to reduced throughput of cattle for human consumption.

**   1997/98 includes income & expense for the period 1 January to 31 March 1998 in respect of the extension of the statutory residues scheme to poultry and fish.

Notes to the Accounts - Continued

Residues continued	1998 £'000	1997 £'000
Non-Statutory Scheme		
Income	1,001	1,109
Staff Costs	(73)	(95)
Depreciation	(5)	(6)
Testing and Collection Costs	(863)	(938)
Other Costs	(43)	(43)
Total income less costs (cost recovery = 101.7%)	17	27
Total residues income less costs (cost recovery = 104.4%)	163	53

Policy	1998 £'000	1997 £'000
Income	1,584	1,546
Staff Costs	(786)	(865)
Depreciation	(53)	(55)
Other Costs	(723)	(584)
Total income less costs (cost recovery = 101.4%)	22	42

In arriving at the cost recovery position for each business area some costs e.g. salaries and training, have been apportioned on the basis of the VMD's work recording system. The results of this exercise during 1997/98 show that staff time was utilised as follows:

	1998 %	1997 %
Licensing	65	64
Policy	27	30
Residues – Statutory	6	3
– Non-Statutory	2	3
Total	100	100

Some costs e.g. residues testing costs have been allocated specifically.

Other costs e.g. legal services have been allocated on the basis of estimated usage.

Notes to the Accounts - Continued

3. DIRECT SUBCONTRACTING COSTS

Amounts charged in the Income & Expenditure Account for subcontractors' costs:

	1998	1997
	£'000	£'000
Costs of licensing and inspection activities payable to the Medicines Control Agency	(155)	(154)
Costs of work performed by the Laboratory of the Government Chemist	(1)	(8)
Costs of the non-statutory residues surveillance, including analysis work performed by the Central Science Laboratory	(863)	(938)
Costs of statutory residues sampling and analysis done by the Veterinary Laboratories Agency and the Central Science Laboratory including samples collected by the Animal Health Veterinary Group and the Meat Hygience Service	(2,312)	(2,326)
	(3,331)	(3,426)

4. STAFF COSTS

(a) Staff costs include:

	1998	1997
	£'000	£'000
Salaries	(2,422)	(2,351)
Social security	(185)	(186)
Superannuation	(359)	(346)
	(2,966)	(2,883)

(b) The average number of staff employed during the year was:

	1998	1997
Scientific	34	33
Administrative	72	73
	106	106

(c) The Chief Executive is employed on a four year contract until 19 August 2001. His total actual remuneration including taxable benefits in 1997/98 was £63,560 (1996/97: £58,613). The Chief Executive is an ordinary member of the Principal Civil Service Pension Scheme. There are no other taxable benefits, compensation or redundancy arrangements payable for premature loss of office.

(d) Members of the Ownership Board, with the exception of the Chief Executive and the external members, are staff from the parent departments (MAFF and the Department of Health). MAFF bears the costs of their representatives and the external members. This cost is included in the notional MAFF overhead charge.

(e) The following number of senior civil servants, including the Chief Executive, received emoluments (excluding pension contributions) falling within the following ranges:

	1998	1997
£60,001 - 65,000	1	-
£55,001 - 60,000	-	1
£50,001 - 55,000	2	-
£45,001 - 50,000	-	2

(f) The number of employees, other than senior civil servants, who received emoluments (excluding pension contributions) in the following ranges was:

	1998	1997
£45,001 - 50,000	1	-
£40,001 - 45,000	5	6
£35,001 - 40,000	7	6
£30,001 - 35,000	9	3

(g) *Pensions*

VMD employees are civil servants to whom the conditions of the Superannuation Acts 1965 and 1972 and subsequent amendments apply. For 1997/98 contributions of £359,000 (1996/97 - £346,000) were incurred at the following rates of superannuable pay:

Band 1	Grades AO and below	11.0%
Band 2	Grades EO to SEO	13.5%
Band 3	Grades 7 to 5	17.5%
Band 4	Grades 4 and above	19.5%

These rates are determined by the Government Actuary and advised by the Treasury.

5. OTHER OPERATING COSTS

	1998	1997
These are made up as follows:	£'000	£'000
Travel and Subsistence	(117)	(141)
Training	(63)	(55)
Provisions for bad debt and other write-offs	(63)	(113)
Other Costs	(863)	(570)
Audit Fees - (notional)	(20)	(20)
Overhead Payments to VLA	(131)	(152)
Insurance – (notional)	(4)	(5)
	(1,261)	(1,056)

6. RESEARCH AND DEVELOPMENT

From 1 April 1991 the VMD took over responsibility for the management of the Research and Development programme on veterinary medicines on behalf of the MAFF policy customer. These costs do not form part of the VMD cost recovery targets, are not reported in the VMD's Income & Expenditure Account, and are not borne by industry.

The work is predominantly commissioned with the Central Science Laboratory and the Veterinary Laboratories Agency and amounts to £1,711,000 (1996/97: £1,880,000).

7. INTEREST ON CAPITAL

Interest on Capital at 6 per cent is calculated in accordance with the Treasury Guidance on Fees and Charges, and is based on the average net assets employed throughout the year, excluding cash in transit to the Ministry.

8. TANGIBLE FIXED ASSETS

	IT Equipment	Office Equipment	Furniture + Fittings	Total
	£'000	£'000	£'000	£'000
Cost or Valuation				
At 1 April 1997	1,284	15	58	1,357
Additions	**283**	**2**	**-**	**285**
Disposals	**(63)**	**(2)**	**-**	**(65)**
At 31 March 1998	**1,504**	**15**	**58**	**1,577**
Depreciation				
At 1 April 1997	(729)	(6)	(34)	(769)
Provided during year	**(195)**	**(1)**	**(6)**	**(202)**
Disposals	**64**	**-**	**-**	**64**
At 31 March 1998	**(860)**	**(7)**	**(40)**	**(907)**
Net Book Value				
At 31 March 1998	**644**	**8**	**18**	**670**
At 31 March 1997	555	9	24	588

Fixed assets have not been revalued on the grounds that the result does not materially change the net book value shown in the balance sheet.

9. DEBTORS AND PREPAYMENTS

		1998	1997
		£'000	£'000
Trade Debtors	– Licensing	315	153
	– Residues	985	610
VAT recoverable		33	11
Prepayments		23	22
		1,356	796

Debtors are shown net of a provision of £481,000 (1996/97: £442,000) for bad and doubtful debts.

10. CASH AT BANK

The VMD collects moneys from its customers, paying the funds into a local bank account with the National Westminster Bank. The funds are then transmitted onward to the Ministry as soon as the National Westminster Bank has cleared the funds. The cash at bank figure represents funds paid in by the VMD but which had not been cleared by the year end.

11. CREDITORS AND INCOME PREPAYMENTS

	1998	1997
	£'000	£'000
Trade Creditors	(175)	(135)
Owing to Government Agencies	(39)	(39)
Income Prepayments	(438)	(176)
	(652)	(350)

It is the VMD's policy to pay invoices not in dispute within 30 days or the agreed contractual terms if otherwise specified. The VMD is a registered supporter of the CBI's Prompt Payers Code of Good Practice.

12. GENERAL FUND

The VMD is funded by the Ministry of Agriculture, Fisheries and Food and the position is shown in the "Financed by" section of the Balance Sheet by means of the General Fund. Within this Fund there are three distinct parts:

– The General Account represents the value of the VMD's net current assets as at 1 April 1991 which is the date from which the Accounts Direction became effective. These net current assets have therefore been built up as a result of prior years' vote funding. Movements in this account reflect funding requirements during the year. This reserve will not be distributable.

– An Insurance Provision has been established by means of a notional insurance charge to the Income and Expenditure Account in accordance with the Treasury Guidance on Fees and Charges. Claims against the VMD would be referred to HM Government but small claims will be offset against this provision, which is included as part of the General Fund, as appropriate.

– The Operating Account represents the accumulated operating cost recovery surplus or deficit transferred from the Income and Expenditure Account

	General Account	Insurance Provision	Operating Account	General Fund
	£'000	£'000	£'000	£'000
Balance at 1 April 1997	826	23	228	1,077
Movements	**136**	**4**	**191**	**331**
Balance at 31 March 1998	**962**	**27**	**419**	**1,408**

13. CAPITAL COMMITMENTS

There were no capital commitments outstanding at year end for which contracts had been entered into or which had been authorised by the Management Group.

14. SENIOR MANAGEMENT INTERESTS

None of the senior management has had any financial interest in the VMD either during the financial year or since.

15. CONTINGENT LIABILITIES

In June 1991 a manufacturer of Veterinary Medicines commenced judicial review proceedings of certain licensing actions by the VMD. The case reached the Court of Appeal in Northern Ireland who in March 1995 referred to the European Court of Justice a number of questions for a preliminary ruling which was given on 2 April 1998. The case is expected to be relisted in the Court of Appeal in Northern Ireland in the Autumn for outstanding issues to be resolved. The applicant has not, as yet, quantified the losses and in the absence of this information it is difficult to assess the financial consequences of the case. Depending on the outcome, the VMD may be liable for costs.

Four individuals commenced proceedings in 1996 and early 1997 against the Ministry, the VMD and others for alleged injuries caused as a result of exposure to organophosphorus sheep dips. Two of the individuals decided to discontinue their proceedings and these have now been formally dismissed. The remaining cases are at an early stage and it is not known when they will be resolved.

Pending the outcome of all the outstanding cases, it is not practicable to make a prudent assessment of any financial consequences they may have.

16. RELATED PARTY TRANSACTIONS

As the VMD is an Executive Agency of the Ministry of Agriculture, Fisheries and Food, the Ministry is regarded as a related party.

During the year, the VMD has had significant material transactions with the Ministry, and with other entities for which the Ministry is regarded as the parent Department, viz:

> The Veterinary Laboratories Agency
>
> The Central Science Laboratory
>
> The Meat Hygiene Service

In addition, the VMD has had various material transactions with other central Government bodies. Most of these transactions have been with the Medicines Control Agency.

None of the board members, key managerial staff or other related parties has undertaken any material transactions with the VMD during the year other than reimbursement for travel and subsistence in the normal course of business.

17. YEAR 2000

The VMD is part of the Ministry of Agriculture, Fisheries and Food's Millennium Compliance Project. The VMD has made a decision in principle to adopt Microsoft Windows NT as its main computer operating environment. The version of the software being adopted is millennium compliant. The VMD has already purchased sufficient computer hardware and software for the conversion which will be undertaken by its own staff. All main databases will be millennium compliant and run in this environment. The VMD's accounting systems are already millennium compliant, running under Microsoft Windows NT.

Veterinary Medicines Directorate

Statement of Agency's and Chief Executive's Responsibilities

Under section 5 of the Exchequer and Audit Departments Act 1921 the Treasury have directed the Veterinary Medicines Directorate to prepare a statement of accounts for each financial year in the form and on the basis set out in the accounts direction on page 84 of these financial statements. The accounts are prepared on an accruals basis and must give a true and fair view of the Agency's state of affairs at the year end and of its income and expenditure total recognised gains and losses and cash flows for the financial year.

In preparing the accounts the Agency are required to:

● observe the accounts direction issued by the Treasury, including the relevant accounting and disclosure requirements, and apply suitable accounting policies on a consistent basis;

● make judgements and estimates on a reasonable basis;

● state whether applicable accounting standards have been followed, and disclose and explain any material departures in the financial statements;

● prepare the financial statements on the going concern basis, unless it is inappropriate to presume that the Agency will continue in operation.

The Accounting Officer for the Ministry of Agriculture, Fisheries and Food has designated the Chief Executive of the Veterinary Medicines Directorate as the Accounting Officer for the Agency. His relevant responsibilities as Accounting Officer, including his responsibility for the propriety and regularity of the public finances and for the keeping of proper records, are set out in the Accounting Officers' Memorandum, issued by the Treasury and published in "Government Accounting".

Veterinary Medicines Directorate

The Certificate and Report of the Comptroller and Auditor General to the House of Commons

I certify that I have audited the financial statements on pages 68 to 81 under the Exchequer and Audit Departments Act 1921. These financial statements have been prepared under the historical cost convention as modified by the revaluation of certain fixed assets and the accounting policies set out on page 72.

Respective responsibilities of the Agency, the Chief Executive and Auditors

As described on page 82 the Agency and the Chief Executive are responsible for the preparation of financial statements and for ensuring the regularity of financial transactions. It is my responsibility to form an independent opinion, based on my audit, on those statements and on the regularity of the financial transactions included in them and to report my opinion to you.

Basis of opinion

I conducted my audit in accordance with Auditing Standards issued by the Auditing Practices Board. An audit includes examination, on a test basis, of evidence relevant to the amounts, disclosures and regularity of financial transactions included in the financial statements. It also includes an assessment of the significant estimates and judgements made by the Agency and Chief Executive in the preparation of the financial statements, and of whether the accounting policies are appropriate to the Agency's circumstances, consistently applied and adequately disclosed.

I planned and performed my audit so as to obtain all the information and explanations which I considered necessary in order to provide me with sufficient evidence to give reasonable assurance that the financial statements are free from material misstatement, whether caused by error, or by fraud or other irregularity and that, in all material respects, the expenditure and income have been applied to the purposes intended by Parliament and the financial transactions conform to the authorities which govern them. In forming my opinion I also evaluated the overall adequacy of the presentation of information in the financial statements.

Opinion

In my opinion:

- the financial statements give a true and fair view of the state of affairs of the Veterinary Medicines Directorate at 31 March 1998 and of the surplus, total recognised gains and losses and cash flows for the year then ended and have been properly prepared in accordance with the Exchequer and Audit Departments Act 1921 and directions made thereunder by Treasury;

- in all material respects the expenditure and income have been applied to the purposes intended by Parliament and the financial transactions conform to the authorities which govern them.

I have no observations to make on these financial statements.

John Bourn
Comptroller and Auditor General

Date 7 July 1998

National Audit Office
157-197 Buckingham Palace Road
Victoria
London SW1W 9SP

Veterinary Medicines Directorate

Accounts Direction given by the Treasury

The Treasury, in pursuance of section 5 of the Exchequer and Audit Departments Act 1921, hereby gives the following Direction:

1. The statement of accounts which it is the duty of the Veterinary Medicines Directorate to prepare in respect of the financial year ended 31 March 1992 and in respect of any subsequent financial year shall comprise:

    a)   a foreword;

    b)   an income and expenditure account;

    c)   a balance sheet; and

    d)   a cash flow statement;

    including in each case such notes as may be necessary for the purposes referred to in the following paragraphs.

2. The Veterinary Medicines Directorate shall observe all relevant accounting and disclosure requirements given in "Government Accounting" and in the Treasury booklet "Trading Accounts: A Guide for Government Departments and Non-Departmental Public Bodies" (the "Trading Accounts booklet") as amended or augmented from time to time.

3. The statement of accounts referred to above shall give a true and fair view of the income and expenditure, state of affairs and cash flow of the Veterinary Medicines Directorate. Subject to the foregoing requirement, the statement of accounts shall also, without limiting the information given and as described in Schedule 1 of this Direction, meet:

    a)   the accounting and disclosure requirements of the Companies Act;

    b)   best commercial accounting practices including accounting standards issued or adopted by the Accounting Standards Board; and

    c)   any disclosure and accounting requirements which the Treasury may issue from time to time in respect of accounts which are required to give a true and fair view; insofar as these are appropriate to the Veterinary Medicines Directorate and are in force for the financial period for which the statement of accounts is to be prepared.

4. Additional disclosure requirements are set out in Schedule 2 of this Direction.

5. The income and expenditure account and balance sheet shall be prepared under the historical cost convention modified by the inclusion of fixed assets at their value to the business by reference to current costs.

18th February 1992
Treasury Officer of Accounts

Schedules 1 and 2 to the Accounts Direction

Schedule 1

Application of the Companies Acts' Requirements

1. The disclosure exemptions permitted by the Companies Act in force for the financial period for which the statement of accounts is to be prepared shall not apply to the Veterinary Medicines Directorate unless specifically approved by the Treasury.

2. The foreword shall contain the information required by the Companies Act to be disclosed in the Directors' Report, to the extent that such requirements are appropriate to the Veterinary Medicines Directorate.

3. In preparing its income and expenditure account and balance sheet, the Veterinary Medicines Directorate shall adopt Format 1 prescribed in Schedule 4 to the Companies Act 1985 to the extent that such requirements are appropriate to the Veterinary Medicines Directorate. Regard should be had to the examples in Annex C of the Trading Accounts booklet, in particular the need to strike the balance sheet totals at "Total Assets less Current Liabilities".

4. The foreword and balance sheet shall be signed and dated.

Schedule 2

Additional Disclosure Requirements

1. The foreword shall state that the accounts have been prepared in accordance with a direction given by the Treasury in pursuance of Section 5 of the Exchequer and Audit Departments Act 1921.

2. The foreword shall include a brief history of the Veterinary Medicines Directorate and its statutory background. Regard should be had to Annexes B and C of the Trading Accounts booklet.

3. The notes to the accounts shall include details of:

   a) recovery of research and development costs from Government funds; and

   b) the key corporate financial targets set by the responsible Minister together with an indication of the performance achieved.

Printed in the UK for The Stationery Office Limited on behalf of the
Controller of Her Majesty's Stationery Office
Dd5068111, 7/98, 39462, Job No 51919